SCHOLASTIC
M
MATHS SKILLS

DEVELOPING MENTAL MATHS

WITH 9-11 YEAR OLDS

TAMARA BIBBY

Published by Scholastic Ltd
Villiers House
Clarendon Avenue
Leamington Spa
Warwickshire CV32 5PR

Text ©1997 Tamara Bibby
© 1997 Scholastic Ltd

2 3 4 5 6 7 8 9 0   8 9 0 1 2 3 4 5 6

SERIES CONSULTANT/AUTHOR
Tamara Bibby

EDITOR
Irene Goodacre

ASSISTANT EDITOR
Lesley Sudlow

SERIES/BOOK DESIGNER
Anna Oliwa

ILLUSTRATIONS
Garry Davies

COVER ARTWORK
James Alexander/David Oliver
(Berkeley Studios)

Designed using Aldus Pagemaker
Printed in Great Britain by Ebenezer Baylis & Son, Worcester

British Library Cataloguing-in-Publication Data
A catalogue record for this book is available from the British
Library.

ISBN 0-590-53765-2

CONTENTS

Mathematics does not exist in the world independent of the people who use it. It exists primarily in people's heads and is, therefore, a mental activity.

Many adults in Britain today remember learning maths in primary school as a repetitive cycle of the teacher demonstrating a method and working through an example on the board, then setting a page of practice 'sums' to reinforce that method. These methods, or algorithms, many of which we still use, were developed so that the clerks and shopkeepers of post-Industrial Revolution Europe could accurately add and subtract, multiply and divide long columns of numbers.

We no longer need to work in that way – the mathematical demands of modern society are very different. We need to be able to read, and make sense of, a much wider range of numerical information – statistics including interest rates and other variable percentages and ratios, as well as the vast array of graphs and charts that have accompanied the computer revolution. Simply being able to apply the four rules of number in a narrow range of situations is no longer adequate.

BECOMING NUMERATE

We need to broaden our perception of numeracy just as we have had to broaden our concept of what it means to be literate. The mathematics taught in primary schools should help pupils to become truly numerate, giving them an ability, and a willingness, to use mathematical skills and tools to tackle numerical problems in flexible and creative ways. A mechanical training in performing basic skills and operations is not enough.

Pupils need to be able to use mathematical skills and tools with equal facility in a wide range of contexts. People who are numerate are able to:
● perform number operations with measures and money as well as out of context (as pages of 'sums');
● deal with numerical information presented in a variety of ways including diagrams, graphs, tables and charts;
● make decisions about whether to work

mentally, on paper, or with a calculator depending on the degree of accuracy needed and the complexity of the task.

THE IMPORTANCE OF MENTAL CALCULATION

Over a period of many years Her Majesty's Inspectors have called for increased attention to be given to mental calculation. They have highlighted an over-reliance on counting methods among older KS2 children, as well as an inability to make sensible estimates (HMCI *Annual Report 1994/95*, for example). Suggestions have been made that teachers need to help children to develop their mathematical language skills as well as a 'feel for number' by using discussion to challenge their understanding. Further emphasis has been placed upon the importance of identifying, analysing and correcting errors and misconceptions in the understanding of number (*The Teaching and Learning of Number in Primary Schools, Mathematics* AT2, 1993).

Recently, the Government became so concerned over the apparent drop in standards in numeracy that they set up twelve national centres to work with schools and teachers to raise standards of attainment (the National Numeracy Project). The Government's concern over standards in numeracy has been echoed by public concern and repeated calls for a return to the teaching of mental maths. These concerns are not new, and were particularly well articulated in the Cockcroft Report (1982).

255 *We believe that the decline of mental and oral work within mathematics classrooms represents a failure to recognise the central place which working 'done in the head' occupies throughout mathematics. Even when using traditional methods of recording calculations on paper, the written record is usually based on steps which are done mentally.*

When working on 'everyday maths' people who are 'mathematically effective' do not use the standard written methods they were taught in school, they work mentally and use personal methods. The Cockcroft Report pointed out that:

256 *Although many pupils come to realise by themselves that methods which may be convenient on paper are often not well suited to use 'in their heads', we believe that in the case of many other pupils it is necessary for the teacher to point out explicitly and to discuss at length the variety of methods which it is possible to use...*

Although many people *do* develop flexible methods on their own this has generally been achieved *in spite of* the teaching they received – the development of a range of flexible methods is rarely explicitly encouraged. Teachers cannot trust to luck – pupils need to be taught to develop a variety of flexible methods which can be used appropriately in different contexts. However, as Cockcroft goes on to say:

> *... no attempt should be made to force a single 'proper method' of performing mental calculations; pupils should be encouraged to make use of whatever methods suit them best. Teachers should also encourage pupils to reflect upon the methods which they develop for themselves so that facility in mental computation can be consolidated and extended.*

The Mathematics National Curriculum (1995) states that:

> *pupils should be given opportunities to develop flexible methods of working with number, orally and mentally.*
> *(KS1 Number 1a)*
>
> *pupils should be given opportunities to develop flexible methods of computation and recording, and use them with understanding; and develop the skills needed for accurate and appropriate use of equipment. (KS2 Number 1a and c)*

and, more specifically:

> *pupils should be taught to develop a variety of mental methods of computation with whole numbers to 100, and explain patterns used; extend mental methods to develop a range of non-calculator methods of computation that involve addition and subtraction of whole numbers, progressing to methods for multiplication and division of up to three-digit by two-digit whole numbers. (KS2 Number 3d)*

The Scottish Guidelines for *Mathematics 5–14* considers 'using mental methods' as a discrete issue in maths teaching, exemplifying the range of methods that might be used for straightforward mental calculation and going on to state that:

> *It is important to recognise that when calculating mentally we often use different methods from those we have used for*

written calculations. We should encourage pupils to develop and practise flexible mental approaches, perhaps by class or group discussion of different ways to carry out particular calculations.

The non-statutory guidance of the National Curriculum (1989) states that:

> 511 *Activities should encourage pupils to use mental arithmetic and to become confident in the use of a range of mathematical tools.*
> ● *The ability to use mental arithmetic in everyday life and work is very important. This includes the vital skills of estimating results in advance, and of checking answers mentally for accuracy and reasonableness.*
> ● *Activities should provide opportunities for pupils to develop skills in selecting and using a wide range of mathematical tools – constructional kits, drawing instruments, measuring equipment, calculating aids, electronic calculators and micro-computers. They should also help pupils to select with confidence the most appropriate ways to tackle different problems.*

The effective and appropriate use of these mathematical tools requires an understanding of likely outcomes and an ability to estimate. The ability to select efficient mathematical tools is a skill needed throughout life – not just in school. As an adult, for example, I might need to keep track of money in a bank account. There are a variety of tools available to help me: these range from spreadsheets, to account books, calculators and bits of paper. The accuracy with which I need to keep track of the money in the account will vary according to circumstances. If, for example, I am saving for a holiday, the money available in a savings account calculated on a piece of paper will probably be sufficiently accurate. If, however, the account is that of a small business with overheads, bills outstanding and suppliers to be paid, then a piece of paper may be less efficient than a spreadsheet. If I do not know how to use a spreadsheet this option is not available to me.

MATHEMATICAL TOOLS AND MENTAL MATHEMATICS

At first sight it may seem like a contradiction to talk about mental maths in the same breath as the use of mathematical tools (such as calculators) and paper and pencil; however it need not be. Imagine the task of estimating the cost of a class visit to a museum – public transport, entrance fees, the number of adults needed to accompany, reduced rates for a group booking and so on – you would undoubtedly make jottings on a scrap of paper, rounding up or down to keep the numbers manageable, working the calculations mentally but keeping note of the stages as the whole is too much to hold in your head. The mathematics is being worked mentally (you are not using paper and pencil algorithms), but the paper and pencil are there to 'extend your mental screen' – to act as an *aide-mémoire*. Without the paper and pencil the task may well be unmanageable.

Similarly, a calculator may be used when the numbers are 'fiddly' or when repeated use of the same operation on several numbers makes the memory facility a boon – as in instances where the steps are simple but long, and the calculations tedious. Here the maths includes both repetitious calculations *and* the understanding of the steps to be taken. As a teacher there is one question you need to answer when deciding whether calculators would be appropriate in tasks that are essentially mental: 'What do I want the class to get out of this activity – practice doing calculations or practice in deciding what mathematics to use?'

FACT OR FIGURING OUT?

Recent research* points to that fact that 'knowing by heart' and 'figuring out' support each other. Working successfully in your head involves using things that you already know to derive new information. In time, the things that you once had to work out are added to the repertoire of things that you know. As your bank of known facts increases it adds to the ways available to you to work things out.

Consider the differences between these different ways of working out 7×7 and what needs to be known for each method.

● Multiplication can be solved by repeated addition:

$$7 + 7 + 7 + 7 + 7 + 7 + 7 = 49$$

● Multiplication of larger numbers can be built up in smaller steps, doubling and subtractions:

	$2 \times 7 = 14$
double	$2 \times (2 \times 7) = 28$
double	$2 \times (4 \times 7) = 56$
subtract	$56 - 7 = 49$

● Multiplication of larger numbers can be built up in smaller steps, 3×7, doubling, and addition:

	$3 \times 7 = 21$
double	$2 \times (3 \times 7) = 42$
add	$42 + 7 = 49$

● Multiplication of larger numbers can be built up in smaller steps, doubling, 5×7, and addition:

$$7 = 5 + 2, so$$
$$(5 \times 7) + (2 \times 7) = 35 + 14 = 49$$

Each method uses known facts and procedures to figure out new information. Not everyone feels able to make this kind of use of the facts they know. Often those who are insecure about their mathematical knowledge would rather use familiar counting methods which seem safer. Many pupils become very adept at developing counting strategies. In the end, however, these are too slow and cumbersome, so pupils need to be encouraged away from them.

Pupils need to be given scope to develop ways of working which allow them to increase their store of known facts, and the strategies they have for using these, to derive new information. They need to be shown ways to develop more efficient and effective strategies – thus moving beyond a reliance on counting. This requires them to take risks, so they will need a 'safe' environment – an environment where their ideas are valued and creative approaches are actively encouraged.

THE NEED TO KNOW AND THE PLACE OF WRITTEN WORK

In helping children to build upon what they know, the facts of which children already have command will need to be tracked. If they are being challenged to work mentally, most children will develop their store of known facts quite spontaneously. However, some facts may prove more difficult for individuals and they will need to make an effort to learn them. The learning of 'recalcitrant' facts may need to be undertaken quite explicitly from time to time.

An example might be the seven times table, with which many children experience difficulty. It is worth considering how you challenge children to commit facts to memory: 'Learn your seven times table' presents quite a daunting task with 10 facts to memorise. On the other hand: 'You know 2, 3, 4, 5 and 10 × 7. You need to learn 6, 7, 8 and 9 × 7. However, you already know half the seven times table facts so you shouldn't have too much difficulty' is much more manageable.

Written work can develop from mental work. As was mentioned earlier, the standard algorithms we use were developed for contexts that are no longer relevant and *nowhere* does the National

Curriculum specify particular methods to be used. Recording mental work is very different to recording calculations out of context (doing pages of already set out 'sums'). You may like to consider the ways in which some of the strategies are recorded in this book as a possible starting point for helping children develop written methods that build on their mental strategies.

STARTING TO USE DISCUSSION

Evidence of pupils' methods of working on mental maths can only be gathered through discussion. It should be noted, however, that there is a significant difference between what may be termed 'question-and-answer sessions' and true 'discussion'. Discussion is more open and allows all participants the right to contribute. It is facilitated by the use of open (rather than closed) questions.

For example, 'How many pairs of numbers can you find which multiply to give 12?' is more challenging than 'What is 3 × 4?' (and demonstrates the difference between an open and a closed question). Questioning which challenges pupils to apply, synthesise or explain their knowledge is much more effective in raising attainment than questioning that merely tests the ability to recall facts and procedures.

When pupils first start to work on developing their mental methods they often respond to questions such as 'How did you do that?' with 'In my head' or 'I don't know'. Such responses *may* mean exactly what they say, however it is more likely that they may indicate:
● disbelief at what you are asking ('I've never been asked this before – I must have misunderstood');
● reluctance to tell the truth because they worked it out in their own way (using a 'non-school' method) and they fear being told off by the teacher;
● reluctance to tell the truth because they fear (peer or teacher) ridicule (they perceive their methods to be strange and assume that others do things differently);
● a lack of vocabulary – ('I know what I did, I just can't explain it');

● a lack of trust or a fear of failure – ('What use is going to be made of my answer?', 'Am I going to get myself into something I can't get out of?').

Overcoming these difficulties and encouraging the children to give longer responses than the traditionally acceptable one word (or number) answer will require patience. Modelling suitable responses either by offering alternatives or by reflecting back what a child has said, helps pupils to develop vocabulary and a sense of what constitutes an acceptable answer. You can offer suggestions which may be aimed at addressing one or more of the points above:

> *'Teachers don't often ask this do they?...'*
> *'I know I would have done that one by.... Is that how you solved it?'*
> *'Did you do it the same way as you would do it on paper or did you use another way?'*
> *'You gave the right answer, I am wondering how you worked it out.'*
> *'I think I understand what you are saying. Did you (rephrase explanation)?'*
> *'Do you think you got the right answer to this? What makes you think your answer is correct?'*

It is important to value all responses while also encouraging pupils to try the more efficient strategies used by their peers, or suggested as possible by yourself:
'Those are all good ways of working it out. Which was the quickest way? ('*Kim's*'.) Can you remember how Kim's method worked? You could try to use that method for this one...'.

Each activity in this book offers specific questions to help you draw out the maths from the children. Where it is appropriate, ways of introducing specific mathematical language and the correct vocabulary are highlighted.

Although at all times you need to guard against turning a mental strategy into another algorithm to learn, it may be necessary to offer a more efficient strategy if it is not being developed by the children. Any strategies that you offer in this spirit need to be added to the range of strategies available rather than being offered to replace the others.

WAIT TIME

The time between asking a question and expecting a response is called 'wait time'. Research[*] has shown that many teachers wait for less than one second before expecting a pupil to answer or moving on to someone else. A wait time of about three seconds significantly improves both the achievement and attitudes of pupils. But getting the wait time right is important. Perhaps surprisingly, waiting too long for an answer can have the effect of decreasing the quality of

interaction between teacher and pupil and reducing the level of pupil achievement.

When thinking about how much wait time to leave, it is important to consider the kind of question you have asked – a test of quick recall requires a shorter wait time than a more challenging question; a single word reply takes less time to formulate than an explanation or a description.

MAKING POSITIVE USE OF INCORRECT ANSWERS

While accuracy is important you can often learn more about a pupil's understanding by discussing incorrect answers. Often teachers avoid doing this because they do not want to deflate or worry a child. However, leaving a pupil knowing they 'got it wrong' can start to build an 'I can't do it' attitude which can be difficult to break later.

In tackling incorrect answers there are a variety of possibilities which need to be considered:

● *Has the question been misunderstood?*
Asked to find the missing number in 7 + ? = 15 an answer of 22 may be given because the 7 and 15 have been added together. This may be due to carelessness or it may result from the child not being able to 'read' a question where the answer is required before the '=' sign.

● *Is the solution procedure used inherently incorrect?*
Asked to solve 'Joan was given £24 for her birthday. She spent £7.50, how much does she have left?', an answer of £23.50 may be given because: 'There is 50p change, then 7 – 4 is 3 and the 20 is left.' This demonstrates significant misunderstandings. The child might go further if pressed to explain: 'Well, I knew there would be 50p because 50p and 50p is £1. Then I looked at the 7 and the 4 and I thought it would be 4 – 7, but I know you can't take a big number from a small number, so I did 7 – 4 and that was 3. And nothing happened in the tens column so that stayed the same.'

● *Has there been an arithmetical error?*
A correct strategy has been used but an inaccuracy has crept in. Asked to solve the problem of Joan's birthday money the following answer may be given: 'Well, if I add 50p, that's £8 and £3 makes £10 and another £14 makes £24 – so that's £17.50 left.' A prompt such as '8 and 3 is 10?' is usually enough to sort this kind of problem out.

It is clear from the examples above that the work you would need to undertake in each instance would be very different. Before working with one child on a particular misconception it is valuable to ask 'Who agrees?' or 'Who else used the same method?' or 'Did anyone else get the same answer?'. It is often worth offering another child the opportunity to explain why they think someone's method has not worked.

THE USE OF PRAISE

Praise is important. We praise positive behaviours to reinforce them, but to be really effective praise needs to be specific. 'Good' and 'Well done' are vague – what was good? Which bit of what I just did, did I do well?

'Well done, you remembered that it is quicker to count on from the largest number. That is much more efficient, isn't it?';

'Good, you explained that very clearly and everyone has understood you. You used all the mathematical terms correctly'.

These are specific – the child is left in no doubt as to what was done well, the positive has been reinforced.

Even where incorrect answers have been reached, praise can be used to boost confidence; 'Well, you got the wrong answer but the strategy was a good one and it would have worked if you hadn't made an arithmetical error.'

DISCUSSION DEVICES

Managing discussions is difficult – especially if you and your class are new to the idea. Here are some things you might find useful to try.
● Count to five in your head before expecting an answer.
● Let the children know you are going to ask lots of people what they think before you all discuss their responses.
● Don't let pupils put their hands up – tell them you will decide who you want to ask.
● Pose a problem to be worked out in pairs.
● Before the pupils report back, give them a time warning: 'In three minutes we are going to hear what everyone has found out. You need to decide who is going to report back and what they are going to say.'.

$$43 + 45 = 88$$
$$3 + 5 = 8$$
$$40 + 40 = 80$$
$$80 + 8 = 88$$

● Encourage pupils to develop a clear style of explanation: 'Did everyone understand what Kay said?', 'Which part of what Kay said are you having difficulty with?', 'Kay, can you explain that a little differently, not everyone understood you', 'Does anyone think they can help Kay?'.

GENERIC QUESTIONS

There are many questions which are generally useful in this type of discussion and some of these are listed below. They may be useful as starting points for discussion about any of the activities in this book. (In addition, each activity in this book has some specific questions suggested alongside.)

What answer did you get?
How did you do that?
Did anyone else use that method?
Did anyone get the same answer by a different method?
Did anyone get a different answer?
How did you get that answer?

Any other answers or methods?

Do you think we can have more than one correct answer for this problem?
Why do you think that?
Does anyone disagree? (Why do you disagree?)

Which answer do we think is correct?
Why is the other answer incorrect?
Why did Sam get a wrong answer?
Can anyone else help Sam to see where she made her mistake?

Do you feel happy about that now Sam?
Can you see your mistake?
How can you remember not to make a similar mistake again?

Which of the methods we used is the most efficient? Why?
Who used that method?
(A number of hands go up.)
Good.
Who thinks they could try that method for this problem?
Who feels they would not be able to use it for this problem?
Can you explain why?
Would one of the people who used this method last time be prepared to work with Carl next time he wants help?

FOLLOW-UP
● Have a 'Fact of the day' and return to it frequently throughout the day.
● Ask how children will remember this in future.
● Ask children what mistake they made and how they will remember not to make it again.
● Ask other children how they might help an individual remember something.
● Ask children to invent mnemonics.

THE ACTIVITIES IN THIS BOOK

The activities in this book are organised into four sections:
● Counting and ordering.
● Addition and subtraction.
● Multiplication and division.
● Multistep and mixed operations.
Each section starts with examples of the sorts of strategies that need to be developed by Years 5 and 6/P6 and 7 in Scotland and Northern Ireland. All the activities that follow can be used as the basis for whole class or group discussions. The activities fall into four categories which reflect decreasing teacher input:

1 Teacher-directed: these are designed to be led exclusively by the teacher with a larger group or whole class. They focus explicitly on number to enable strategies to be discussed. They may be used as assessment activities.

2 Problems: these focus on number in context. The strategies will need to be applied. They may be teacher-directed or worked on collaboratively by small groups or pairs of children.

3 Investigations: these focus on number and algebra, and are designed to encourage pupils to generalise their findings.

4 Games: these are designed to be used by pairs or small groups of pupils independently. They allow pupils to develop strategies in a less formal context.

FURTHER READING
*Askew M & Wiliam D, *Recent Research in Mathematics Education 5–16*, London, HMSO

STRATEGIES

CHILDREN SHOULD BE WORKING WITH NUMBERS OF THE ORDER:

YEAR 5/PRIMARY 6

Counting:
● forwards and backwards in steps of any size using both positive and negative numbers with confidence;
● any fractional chain;
● in decimal increments of tenths and hundredths in steps of 1, 2, 5, 10, 100 and so on ('one point two, one point four, one point six, one point eight, two point zero...' and so on).

Reading and ordering:
● and knowing the value of digits in numbers to at least one million;
● negative numbers;
● unitary fractions including tenths and hundredths ($\frac{1}{2}, \frac{1}{34}, \frac{1}{100}, \frac{1}{56}$ and so on);
● decimals with the same number of decimal places (12.34, 12.07, 1.40, 1.04 and so on).

YEAR 6/PRIMARY 7

Counting:
● forwards and backwards in steps of any size (integer, decimal or fractional).

Reading and ordering:
● and knowing the place value of the digit in any number, including decimals;
● a set of mixed numbers (for example 174, 17.4, 7.14, 1.74, 0.174, 74.1, 1.004, 74.01);
● mixed and vulgar fractions (including tenths and hundredths), converting between the two if necessary.

There is a tendency to stop working with children on counting once they have mastered counting on and back in 1s, 2s, 5s and 10s at the end of Key Stage 1 or early in Key Stage 2. It is important to continue counting.

Often counting back stops at 0 and counting on stops at 100. However, it is quite challenging, for example, to count in 2000s from 23 145, this can help children get to grips with higher order place value names. Similarly counting back in hundredths from 1.82, back in three hundredths from 0.12, or on in halves from −12 may provide an appropriate challenge to older children.

Reading numbers correctly requires an understanding of the place value involved. Discourage children from reading large numbers digit-by-digit as in a telephone number.

> Encourage 'Twenty-two million, six hundred and two thousand and forty-three' NOT '2-2 6-0-2-0-4-3' ('Two, two, six, zero, two...').

Decimal numbers are the exception to this general rule about reading numbers. Digits to the right of the decimal place are read as individual digits:

> 43.56 should be read as 'forty-three point five six' NOT 'forty-three point fifty-six'.

Confusingly, there are other ways of reading this decimal number. These might include: 'forty-three and fifty-six hundredths' or, in the context of money, forty-six pounds and fifty-six pence.

Place value determines the value of a digit by its position in a number. The children should be aware of this, the relative sizes of the digits and the role of 0 as place holder.

Consider the values of the 2s in 2042.02 – one is a thousand times greater and the other a hundred times smaller than the 2 in the units position, and they are both 'kept in place' with 0s to indicate the 'empty' positions.

Consider the full implications of place value – we commonly state that there are 'four 10s' in 2042, this is not strictly correct; there is indeed a 4 in the '10s position' but there are 204 tens in 2042.

Similarly: 12 345 comprises 12 345 ones, 1 234 tens, 123 hundreds, 12 thousands and one ten thousand.

Patterns should be highlighted and discussed with the children wherever they occur. These patterns help children generalise rules for manipulating numbers and can act both as a check and become part of a more general 'sense of number'.

Counting on in 10s: 28 + 30 = 28, 38, 48, 58... (same unit)

Counting on in 5s: 27 + 25 = 27, 32, 37, 42, 47, 52... (alternate units)

Counting on in 1 000s: 23 213, 24 213, 25 213... (thousands digit only changing)

Counting on in steps of an odd number: always alternate odd/even numbers.

Fractions: mental maths activities involving fractions should emphasise fractions as numbers as well as parts of a whole; on its own the 'slices of cake' model often leaves children thinking fractions are not real numbers. Quite early on in fraction work children should become comfortable relating fractions to their decimal equivalents.

Resources for counting and ordering are not only useful in Key Stage 1/P1–3. Number lines and 100 squares, or other 10 × 10 number grids (for example 0–1 in hundredths) are valuable resources for older children. A variety is important because some will work better for different children. They are also useful in that the strong working images of number that they give children can be used as a starting point for work on mental addition and subtraction.

COUNTING AND ORDERING

CARRY ON COUNTING

†† *Whole class* ⏱ *5 minutes*

AIM
To help pupils develop the ability to count in steps of any size.

WHAT TO DO
Tell the class you are all going to do some counting. You can either work round in a circle, or point to the child who should say the next number. If the class has never done this before then start with an increment that everyone will be able to manage until they get the feel of what is happening (possibly counting in 10s).

Choose an increment and a direction (up or down) for counting. In Y5 children should be confident to count with positive and negative numbers, fractions and decimal increments (tenths or hundredths). It is always easier to count from 0 (zero), or from another positive whole number. A progression for counting in halves might be to count forward and then backwards: from 0, from $2\frac{1}{2}$, from $-4\frac{1}{2}$, from $4\frac{1}{4}$, from $-10\frac{1}{8}$ ... and so on. By Y6 children should feel confident counting in steps of any size.

To illustrate, imagine you were counting back in tenths from 2.37 (2.37, 2.27, 2.17, 2.07, 1.97 and so on). Note that these numbers should be read as 'two point three seven' **not** 'two point thirty seven'. Although we read money in that way it is incorrect in other contexts; the .37 is not 'thirty seven' unless you want to read it as '37 hundredths'.

DISCUSSION QUESTIONS
● *If we count for two minutes, where do you think we will get to?*
● *If we carry on counting, will we say –324.97? How about –456.72?*
● *Why do you think that?*

ASSESSMENT QUESTIONS
You just said (6.34). If we carry on what will the (tenth) person say?
(Replace brackets as appropriate.)

EXTENSIONS
Consider counting with:
● positive and negative numbers ('Count up in 100s from –432': –432, –332, –232, –132, and so on);
● fractions including improper or mixed fractions ($\frac{3}{2}$, $\frac{6}{2}$, $\frac{9}{2}$, $\frac{12}{2}$, or $1\frac{1}{2}$, 3, $4\frac{1}{2}$, 6, $7\frac{1}{2}$ and so on);
● decimal increments (1.09, 1.08, 1.07 and so on);
● larger numbers ('Count in 120s from 13 000', 'Count back in 300s from 12 900').

READ A BIG ONE

†† *Whole class* ⏱ *5 minutes*

AIM
To help children learn to read very large numbers.

WHAT TO DO
Write a four- or five-digit number on the board and ask someone to read it out (as a number, rather than as a string of digits). The habit of using commas to divide up groups of three digits can cause confusion with decimal points. One way to avoid this is to separate the groups of three with a gap. So a five-digit number might be written 12 345 ('twelve thousand, three hundred and forty five').

Ask the child how he or she knew how to read the number – which names attach to which digits?

Gradually increase the number of digits, asking different children to read the numbers and go through the naming procedure. Encourage the others to listen carefully to make sure mistakes are not made.

Once you get over the millions, the naming sequence continues up to a thousand million, at which point confusion sets in. Traditionally, in the UK, the sequence continues in the normal way until a million million (1 000 000 000 000 or 10^{12}) is reached: we call this a billion, but Americans consider this to be a trillion, as to them one thousand million (1 000 000 000 or 10^9) is a billion.

The American place value naming system is becoming more prevalent over here (and so the confusion worsens) – how much easier to be a billionaire with the American system! You should choose one system to follow, but it is an interesting point and one worth raising with your class.

As long as you stick with one system there shouldn't be a problem (the British system may be easier to follow because the integrity of the number system is maintained).

You should also use numbers with a lot of decimal places: 987.654 321.

DISCUSSION QUESTIONS
Consider the decimal 987.654 321:
● *What is the value of the 5 in this number? Can you explain why?*
● *If we wanted to change the 4 into 0 with a calculation, how could we do it?*
(subtract 0.004 or add 0.006)
● *How do we read that number?*
● *Can you tell me what number will be 0.001, 10, 100, 10 000 more than this number?*

ASSESSMENT
Read out a very large number and ask someone to write it up on the board so that everyone can see it. Read the number again so that the class can make sure it has been written correctly (for example 'Six hundred and eighty five thousand, nine hundred and twenty one' 685 921).

EXTENSIONS
● Introduce index notation – allowing for the differences in US and UK naming conventions!
● You might like to go on to the investigation 'Index notation' on page 16.

ORDER, ORDER!

†† *Whole class*   ⏱ *5–10 minutes*

AIM
To help children learn to order any set of numbers.

YOU WILL NEED
A series of about ten suitable numbers written on pieces of paper large enough for everybody to be able to read them when they are held up.

WHAT TO DO
The numbers you choose for this activity do not need to be consecutive or evenly spaced. Examples of the kinds of numbers you use might include:
● whole numbers, both positive and negative (4987, 1234, 1290, 1269, –2345 and so on);
● proper fractions (where the numerator is smaller than the denominator), unitary fractions such as $\frac{1}{2}$, $\frac{1}{5}$, $\frac{1}{9}$ and non-unitary fractions such as $\frac{2}{3}$, $\frac{4}{5}$ or $\frac{3}{5}$;
● improper and mixed fractions ('top heavy' fractions or fractions with whole numbers) such as $\frac{3}{2}$, $1\frac{1}{4}$, $\frac{7}{2}$ or $4\frac{5}{8}$;
● decimal fractions to one decimal place, to two

decimal places and so on, as well as mixed numbers of decimal places.

(See the section on the 'Strategies' page 10 'Children should be working with numbers of the order...'.)

When ordering negative numbers, emphasise that –900 is smaller than –9. If you think of the numbers on a number line then it is easy to see that –9 is further to the right, and therefore larger.

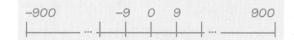

Give one of the numbered pieces of paper to each of two children and ask them to hold these up for everyone to see. One by one, give out the other numbers, allowing time for the children to position themselves in the right order to form a human number line.

DISCUSSION QUESTIONS
● *Are they in the right order?*
● *How can you be sure?*
● *What is the biggest number we have here? What is the smallest?*
● *Which numbers come into the smaller half of the series? How can you tell?*

ASSESSMENT QUESTION
Can anyone give me a number that might go between these two numbers?

EXTENSIONS
● Ordering decimals gets more difficult if the set of decimals you use has a mixed number of decimal places. So, for instance, it is harder to order 1.07, 1.7, 12.7 and 17.02, than to order 1.07, 1.70, 12.70, and 12.07. Similarly, it is easier to order fractions which are of a type (and so easily converted to each other – say halves and quarters) than a mixed set of fractions.
● Try 'Fraction ladders' on page 14 or play 'Decimal ladders' or 'Fraction lines' on page 17.

BETWEEN THE LINES

†† Whole class ⏱ 5 minutes

AIM

To continue to develop understanding of ordering and the continuous nature of number.

WHAT TO DO

Choose and write up two consecutive numbers (or fractions) with a small gap between them and, pointing between them, ask: 'What number could go in here?' Suitable numbers might include: 3 and 4, 27 and 27.1, 43.1 and 43.2, 3.01 and 3.02, $\frac{1}{7}$ and $\frac{2}{7}$, –6 and –7, $\frac{1}{6}$ and 0.2 and so on. (See the section on the 'Strategies' page 10 'Children should be working with numbers of the order...'.)

Choose another pair of numbers and repeat.

The children should come to realise that by increasing the number of decimal places the number sequence becomes infinite.

DISCUSSION QUESTIONS

● How many numbers do you think exist between these two numbers?
● If –6.5 exists between –6 and –7, can you give me a number between –6 and –6.5?

ASSESSMENT QUESTIONS

● Could 34.7 exist between 34 and 35?
● Which would it be closer to on the number line?

EXTENSIONS

● Play 'Fraction lines' on page 17.
● Ask the children to write up the activity using the writing frame photocopiable sheet on page 64.

FRACTION LADDERS

†† Whole class ⏱ 10–20 minutes

AIM

To help the children to develop strategies for ordering fractions and recognising equivalence of fractions.

YOU WILL NEED

A set of fraction cards containing all the possible combinations of halves, quarters and eighths ($\frac{1}{2}$, $\frac{2}{2}$, $\frac{1}{4}$, $\frac{2}{4}$, $\frac{3}{4}$, $\frac{4}{4}$, $\frac{1}{8}$, $\frac{2}{8}$, $\frac{3}{8}$, ...$\frac{8}{8}$).

The cards should be large enough that everyone will be able to see them.

WHAT TO DO

Explain to the children that you have a set of fractions written out on cards that you are going to hand to individuals. Children who are given a card should come to the front of the class and stand in order. Point out that the number line should start with the smallest number. Give out the first two cards (making sure that these are not equivalent fractions) and ask the children to come to the front of the class. Make sure that they are standing in the correct order holding the cards so that everyone else can see them.

Hand out each subsequent card in turn, asking the children to make sure that people stand in the right order. When equivalent fractions come up ask the class to decide what should be done (children could, for example, stand in front of the equivalent, or sit at the feet of and so on).

DISCUSSION QUESTIONS

● Where will you stand?
● Why have you stood in front of her?
● Can you explain how you know those fractions are equivalent?

ASSESSMENT QUESTIONS

● Can you tell me a fraction that could go in here (between two adjacent cards, for example $\frac{6}{8}$ and $\frac{7}{8}$)?
● Can you tell me another fraction that would be equivalent to this one?

VARIATION

Play with other fraction families, such as thirds, sixths, and twelfths.

EXTENSION

Play with a mixed set of fractions, decimal fractions, and percentages (for example $\frac{1}{2}$, $\frac{2}{7}$, 0.9, 0.51, 25%, 51% and so on).

COUNTING AND ORDERING

LIBRARIES

†† *Individuals or small groups*
🕐 *10–20 minutes*

AIM

To allow pupils to use very large numbers in context and to have a chance to operate with large numbers.

WHAT TO DO

Write up this table where everyone can see it.

Public libraries – books stock 1995–96	Total number of books	Total number of children's books
Barnet	999 580	732 799
Belfast	1 460 341	320 612
Derbyshire	1 590 150	794 419
Glasgow	2 247 330	602 294
Gloucestershire	966 204	483 134
Hampshire	3 260 252	1 655 846
Kent	2 843 821	2 515 881
North Eastern	1 044 546	586 418
North Yorkshire	1 268 199	620 692
Staffordshire	1 803 639	1 357 709

Ask questions such as:

● Rounding to the nearest 100 000, how many more books does the biggest library board have than the smallest?

● How many more books do the libraries in Belfast have than the libraries in Barnet?

● How many more children's books are there in the libraries in Kent than the libraries of Gloucestershire?

● What is the difference between the number of books in the biggest and second biggest library stocks?

Ask them to order the libraries from largest to smallest based on total book stock. Then again on the basis of the number of children's books.

DISCUSSION QUESTIONS

● *How are you going to do the ordering?*
● *How do you know that is the largest number?*
● *How did you work out the differences?*
● *Did anyone do it differently?*
● *Which is the most effective method? Why?*

EXTENSIONS

These questions will involve the children in considering proportion. They will need to round the numbers and either talk about ratio, fractions or percentages.

● *In Derbyshire do you have more choice as an adult reader or as a child reader?*
(both the same as 50% of books are children's)

● *In relation to adult readers, in which county are the reading interests of children best served? Why do you say that?*
(Kent – nearly 90% of books are children's books)

● *In which county or region are the reading interests of the adults best served?*
(Belfast – only 22% of books are children's)

You could also challenge the children to explore questions such as:

● *How many books are there in our school library? How many times bigger is the book stock in the libraries in Hampshire?*

● *How many metres of shelving must there be in the children's book sections of the libraries in North Yorkshire?*

● *How fast can you read? How long might it take you to read all the children's books in Barnet?*

● *If you could read a book a day how long would it take you to read all the books in the libraries in Staffordshire?*
(about 5000 years)

● *How many more books are held in England and Wales than in Northern Ireland? Is this a fair comparison?*

Further statistics are provided on photocopiable page 57 and in the table below – these will offer unlimited scope for questions of this type.

Country	Total Bookstock	Total Children's books	% of Children's Books of Total Bookstock
England and Wales	21 711 000	86 479	25
Scotland	2 784 000	10 496	27
Northern Ireland	657 000	2 278	29
United Kingdom	25 152 000	99 253	25

COUNTING AND ORDERING

INDEX NOTATION

†† *Individuals or pairs* ⏲ *About 45 minutes*

AIM
To consider how index notation is written and how it is used in calculations with very large numbers.

WHAT TO DO
Show the children how to write several numbers in these three different ways. You might like to use the chart below:

Name	Numerals	Index notation
one thousand	1 000	1×10^3
ten thousand	10 000	1×10^4
one hundred thousand	100 000	1×10^5
one million	1 000 000	1×10^6

Ask the children how they think index notation might work – how do they think ten million might be written in index notation?

It is important to point out that, just as 7^3 means $7 \times 7 \times 7$, so $\times 10^3$ means $10 \times 10 \times 10$. Repeatedly multiplying by 10 gives the appearance of 'adding zeros' but really the number is moving in relation to the decimal place.

Ask how else they might write 4.56×10^2 (456), or 34.52×10^3 (34 520).

When the children seem happy with this idea, ask them to investigate what happens to the index notation when you multiply and divide by powers of 10. For example: 'If 100 (10^2) is multiplied by 1 000 (10^3) what do you get? How would you write that with index notation?'

Note: You might like to point out to the children that, while $22\ 345 \times 10^3$ is acceptable for 22 345 000, it is more formally correct to use 2.2345×10^7, a decimal with a single-digit whole number and the appropriate power.

DISCUSSION QUESTIONS
● *Why do you think scientists might prefer to write numbers like this?*
● *Who can write 2.4×10^6? Can you read this number?*
(twenty-four million)
● *How would you write 'three hundred and twenty thousand, six hundred and two' in index notation?*
($3.2\ 602 \times 10^5$)
● *What happens if we divide numbers? How about 10 000/10?*
($1 \times 10^4 \div 1 \times 10^1 = 1 \times 100^3$)

● *Have you found a rule you can generalise?*
(When you multiply two powers of 10, you add the powers:
$10^2 \times 10^3 = 10^5$ or $100 \times 1\ 000 = 100\ 000$,
$10^3 \times 10^3 = 10^6$ or $1\ 000 \times 1\ 000 = 1\ 000\ 000$.
When you divide one number by another you subtract the powers:
$10^4 \div 10^2 = 10^2$ or $10\ 000 \div 100 = 100$,
$10^4 \div 10^3 = 10$ or $10\ 000 \div 1000 = 10$.)

ASSESSMENT QUESTIONS
● *How could I express 22 345 000 in index notation?*
($22\ 345 \times 10^3$, 22.345×10^6 or 2.2345×10^7)
● *What would $3.412 \times 10^3 \times 100$ be?*
(3.412×10^5 or 341 200)

EXTENSIONS
● Decimals can also be expressed with index notation. The way this works can be inferred by using division: $10/100 = 0.1$, $10^1/10^2 = 10^{-1}$.
So, 1×10^{-1} is one tenth, 1×10^{-2} is one hundredth and so on.
● Ask the children if they can think of measurements which require very large or very small numbers (distances to planets, dimensions of planets, mountains measured in centimetres, dimensions of atoms, widths of hairs and so on).
● Challenge them to use an encyclopaedia to find examples of such measurements, express these as numbers and also as index notation. Then ask questions such as 'How many times thicker is Pluto than a human hair?' 'How is that best written?'
● Ask the children to write up the activity using the writing frame photocopiable sheet on page 64.

$£1 \times 10^3$
$£1 \times 10^4$
$£1 \times 10^5$

FRACTION LINES

†† Pairs ⏲ 15–30 minutes

AIM

To familiarise the children with the conversion of decimals to fractions and to help them to develop strategies for ordering fractions.

YOU WILL NEED

For each pair – a 0–1 number line marked with ten unnumbered intervals, a calculator, a different-coloured felt-tipped pen for each child.

HOW TO PLAY

The aim is to get three fractions in a row on the number line and to stop your opponent doing the same.

Player 1 chooses two numbers from 1 to 9 and uses these to form a fraction by placing one above the other, for example:

> If 3 and 5 are chosen he might form $\frac{3}{5}$.
> He then uses the calculator to convert the fraction into a decimal ($\frac{3}{5} = 0.6$) and marks this fraction on the number line.

Player 2 now takes her turn.

DISCUSSION QUESTIONS

● *Where do you want to go next? What fraction would allow you to go there?*
● *Can you block your opponent? How?*
● *Can you predict where your fractions will come on the number line?*
● *Is it easier to play strategically with fractions or decimals? Why?*
● *How can you plan a fraction to go between any two others?*
● *Does it matter who starts? Why?*

EXTENSIONS

● Extend the number line to 2 and allow 'top heavy' fractions such as $\frac{3}{2}$.
● Increase the number of fractions that need to be in the row on the number line to 5 to win.

DECIMAL LADDERS

†† Two to four players
⏲ About 10 minutes per round

AIM

To help children learn to order decimals.

YOU WILL NEED

For each child – a ladder baseboard (as shown below) with ten spaces, each big enough to hold a decimal card.

For each group – a set of decimal cards (enough to allow ten per child) numbered from 0–3, initially with one decimal place (0.6, 1.7, 2.9 and so on), moving on to two decimal places (0.12, 1.65, 2.98 ...), and eventually a mixture of decimal places (0.04, 0.4, 1.34, 2 ...).

HOW TO PLAY

The aim of the game is for each player to get as many cards as possible on to his ladder board.

Shuffle the cards and place them face down on the table. Tell the children the highest and lowest cards (0 and 3). The players, one by one, turn over a card and position it on their ladders. A card, once placed, cannot be moved. If a child turns over a card she cannot place she puts it beside her baseboard and play continues.

DISCUSSION QUESTIONS

● *Why have you chosen to place that card there?*
● *How much space should you leave between these cards?*
● *What does anyone else think?*
● *Why have you been unable to place that card?*

VARIATION

Use cards with different numbers of decimal places (see above).

EXTENSION

Cards with mixed numbers of decimal places (0.12, 0.1, 0.123) are more difficult to order than sets with the same number of decimal places.

STRATEGIES

CHILDREN SHOULD BE WORKING WITH NUMBERS OF THE ORDER:

YEAR 5/PRIMARY 6
● add or subtract a single-digit number from any two- or three-digit number eg 32 – 9, 78 + 4;
● add or subtract any two two-digit numbers less than 50 eg 12 + 39, 48 – 23;
● add or subtract multiples of 10 from any two- or three-digit number eg 764 + 50, 345 – 60;
● use negative numbers in context;
● add or subtract two numbers with one decimal place, in the context of measures or money where the units are the same eg 43.2m + 78.5m, or £8.60 – £3.50.

YEAR 6/PRIMARY 7
● add or subtract any two two-digit numbers eg 52 + 49, 72 – 39;
● add two three-digit numbers;
● subtract a two-digit number from a three-digit number;
● add or subtract numbers with two decimal places (with no more than four digits in total) in the context of measures or money where the units are the same eg 4.56km + 13.28km, £7.23 – £3.79;
● use knowledge of equivalence of fractions to add and subtract simple fractions eg $\frac{1}{3}+\frac{2}{9}$.

AS A MINIMUM, BY THE END OF YEAR 6/PRIMARY 7 MOST CHILDREN SHOULD:

● know and use addition and subtraction facts to 20;
● add a series of one-digit numbers;
● approximate answers to calculations by rounding;
● know and use simple fractions eg $\frac{1}{2}, \frac{1}{3}, \frac{1}{4}, \frac{1}{5}, \frac{1}{6}, \frac{1}{8}, \frac{1}{10}$;
● know and use decimals to at least one and then two decimal places in the context of measures and money;
● know and use the 24-hour clock and timetables.

Children will already have a range of mental strategies for addition and subtraction developed earlier with more familiar numbers. These now need to be extended. Many things can slow children down and stop them developing more efficient and effective methods, but the single most significant is a lack of known facts to draw upon. Then they need to be able to select an appropriate strategy to suit the problem; for example, counting on can be an effective subtraction strategy but is not efficient for 3007 – 9.

STRATEGIES FOR ADDITION

Bridging through a decade uses multiples of 10 and makes use of complements (number bonds) within 10 or 20.

> 67 + 35 is solved using 3 + 7 = 10 by splitting the 5 (from the 35) into 3 and a 2:
> 67 + 35 → 67 + 3 = 70, then add
> 70 + 30 + 2; or, 67 + 35 → 35 + 5 = 40,
> then add 40 + 60 + 2.

A more sophisticated 'bridge' might be:

> 78 + 27 → 78 + 22 = 100
> 100 + 5 = 105

Partitioning splits numbers into 10s and 1s using place value:

> 24 + 37 → 20 + 30 + 7 + 4

This can be developed so that only the smaller number is split:

> 24 + 37 → 37 + 20 + 4

Partitioning and rearranging is a further refinement (though rarely used) where the numbers are split up into 10s and 1s and then recombined to give the largest possible 'larger' number:

> 27 + 52 → 57 + 20 + 2

Using known facts can simplify problems:

> 75 + 30   'I know 75 and 25 is 100, so 75 and 30 must be 105.'
> Or   'I know 7 and 3 is 10, so 10 and 30 is 100 and 5 more is 105.'

Using known facts flexibly: doubles

$35 + 38$ → the 38 is recognised as very close to 35 so a known double can be used:
$35 + 38$ → $(2 \times 35) + 3$

Using known facts flexibly: compensating

Alternatively, for the above example, round the 38 up to 40 and compensate for this alteration at the end:

$35 + 38$ → $(35 + 40) - 2$

Using known facts flexibly: finding pairs to make 10 is mostly used when digits are listed in column form. This strategy rearranges strings of single digits into 10s or 5s.

$2 + 6 + 7 + 1 + 8 + 9 + 3 + 4 + 4 + 4 + 2$
→ $2 + 8$, $6 + 4$ and so on, for example to give $(2 + 7 + 1) + (8 + 2) + (3 + 4 + 4 + 4) + (6 + 9)$ or $10 + 10 + 15 + 15 = 50$.

STRATEGIES FOR SUBTRACTION

Counting on Adapting mental strategies to paper can be difficult for children as there is no sign for 'add on', particularly given the efficiency and frequency with which they use the 'counting on' method for subtraction (also called 'shopkeeper's addition' because it is similar to the way change is counted out). Here is one way of recording it:

```
75 – 38                38
            + 2
                       40
            +30
                       70
            + 5
                     _____
                       75
            +37
```

Counting back is a variation on this:

```
75 – 38 is solved as
            75
                    – 5
            70
                    – 30
            40
                    – 2
            38      _____
                    – 37
```

Partitioning, as in the addition strategy, uses place value to split numbers into 10s and 1s:

$74 – 42$ is broken into $70 – 40$ and $4 – 2$

It might not be necessary or sensible to break the numbers up so completely:

$34 – 27$ is broken into:
$(30 – 27) + 4$ or $(34 – 20) – 7$

For larger numbers such as $174 – 48$, the 100 can be 'kept on one side' as it will be unchanged.

Bridging back through a decade:

In solving $75 – 38$ the 8 is split into 5 and 3, so the 5 can be subtracted from the 75 to take it back to a decade number which is easier to deal with:
$75 – 38$ becomes $75 – 5 = 70$ then $(70 – 30) – 3 = 37$

Compensation involves changing numbers to make them more manageable and allowing for the alteration at a later stage. An obvious example would be taking away 9 from a number by subtracting 10 and then adding 1:

$20 – 9 = (20 – 10) + 1$

Also $75 – 38$ is solved as:
$(75 – 40) + 2$ or $(75 – 35) – 3$

$73 – 28$ is solved as $(73 – 30) + 2$

Using other addition facts or doubles:

In solving $82 – 43$, it is recognised that 41 is half of 82 so the answer is derived from this, then the additional 2 is subtracted to compensate:
$82 – 43 = (41 + 41) – (41 + 2)$

ADDITION AND SUBTRACTION

WORK IT OUT

†† *Whole class* ⏱ *10–15 minutes*

AIM
To focus on the development of strategies for addition and subtraction.

WHAT TO DO
From the section headed 'Children should be working with numbers of the order' on page 18, choose pairs of numbers within the children's capabilities. Use them to make up three problems with the second and third problems slightly more challenging than the first, varying the numbers a little if this helps.

Work through the three problems, one at a time. Write each one up on the board, so everyone can see the numbers being discussed. Ask the children about the first one and discuss their answers and methods before moving on. For example: *'How can I work out 73 + 9, 73 + 90, 7.3 + 0.9, or 42 – 8, 245 – 80, 23 – 1.7?'*

DISCUSSION QUESTIONS
The generic questions on page 9 are a good place to start the discussion.
● *Did anyone else get the same answer?*
● *What method did you use?*
● *Which of these methods is most efficient? Why?*
● *What problems did you have? Does anyone have a way around that problem?*

ASSESSMENT QUESTION
How could you use a calculator to work out 98 – 54 if the 'minus' button was broken?
(count on from 54)

EXTENSIONS
● Change the range of the numbers you use.
● Encourage children to try each other's, or one of your own, strategies (but never try to force this).

THROUGH THE DOOR

†† *Whole class* ⏱ *5 minutes*

AIM
To practise the addition of a string of digits and to develop strategies for tracking simultaneous additions.

WHAT TO DO
Tell the class to close their eyes and imagine a door. People are going to start going in through the door in a minute: their task is to keep count of the total number of people. Every time the total reaches a multiple of ten they must put their hand up.

Call out a succession of numbers such as 3, 8, 9, 4, 2, 3, 6, 2, 3, and so on. (Multiples of ten are underlined.) Allow a moment for the calculation to be completed but not enough time to count in ones.

Now tell the children to imagine there are two doors, one on the right and one on the left. This time they must keep track of the numbers of people going through each door. Read out a series of numbers, remembering to say which door they have gone in through, for example:

> 5 in the right, 2 in the left
> 4 in the right, 0 in the left
> 1 in the right, 1 in the left
> 2 in the right, 7 in the left... and so on.

Note: This activity is initially very tricky but, with practice, children can become very good at it. It is useful to be able to hold numbers in your head when you work mentally, so this activity is the mental equivalent of keeping fit!

DISCUSSION QUESTIONS
● *Which was more difficult? Why?*
● *What mental images did you use to help you with the first part of the activity when there was only one door?*
● *What imagery did you use for the second part? How was that different?*
● *Which strategies work best?*
● *How can you remember to try that next time we play this game?*

ASSESSMENT

You can judge who is keeping up accurately as hands go up for multiples of ten.

EXTENSIONS

● Similarly, add money by putting coins into a purse.
● Start at 50 and subtract single-digit numbers.

MULTIPLES OF 10 AND 100

†† *Whole class* ⏱ *10–15 minutes*

AIM

To develop strategies for the addition of multiples of 10.

WHAT TO DO

Randomly generate numbers to fit within a type.
● a three-digit number +/– a two-digit multiple of 10, for example 465 +/– 50, 247 +/– 70;
● a three-digit multiple of 10 +/– a three-digit multiple of 10, for example 270 +/– 160, 420 +/– 280;
● a four-digit multiple of 100 +/– a four-digit multiple of 100, for example 3400 +/– 2200, 3200 +/– 1900.

Generate number sentences, aiming to achieve a balance over where the unknown item appears. For example:

> ? +/– 60 = 240, 470 – ? = 160, 380 + ? = 760, as well as the more usual 830 +/– 220 = ?

DISCUSSION QUESTIONS

Use the generic questions on page 9 to elicit the strategies the children are using to find the unknown.
● *Are you using the same strategies that you would use for smaller numbers?*
● *Why does that work? Can you explain it to me?*
When eliciting strategies it is important to encourage the correct use of language. We often

solve problems such as 340 + 270 by saying '4 and 7 is 11' when what we really mean in this context is '40 and 70 is 110. As long as the children accept and understand this abbreviation there is no problem, but it needs to be very clear to everyone listening what the numbers actually are. If there is any confusion insist that the correct words are used at all times.

EXTENSIONS

● This activity could be consolidated as written work. Children might use a pack of 10–100 cards to generate their own problems by picking two numbers, multiplying both by 10 or 100 and adding or subtracting as needed. For example, (34) and (47) can be used to make 340 + 470 or 470 – 340.
● Similar three-digit numbers +/– multiples of 10 questions can be generated with 1–9 cards and a set of 'decade' cards. Deal three single-digit cards for the three-digit number and draw a decade card for the multiple of 10.
● Encourage the children to write up the strategies used on the writing frame photocopiable sheet given on page 64.

MAKE IT WHOLE

†† *Whole class* ⏱ *5–10 minutes*

AIM

To consider the addition of decimal numbers and complements within 1 (0.1 + 0.9 and so on).

WHAT TO DO

Shuffle two sets of 0–9 cards and deal two cards. Use these to make a two-digit number with one decimal place (for example, with a 3 and 7 you could make 3.7 or 7.3).

Write the decimal number up so everyone can see it and ask 'What do we need to add to this to make the next whole number?'

Insist on correct language – so for 3.7, the answer would be either 'nought point three' or 'three tenths'.

Note: 'Complements within 1' is the correct terminology here, but you may hear these bonds referred to as 'complementary pairs'.

DISCUSSION QUESTIONS

● *How do you know?*
● *What knowledge are you using?*

ASSESSMENT QUESTION

I had to add 0.8 to my number to make it up to 4, what number did I start with?

ADDITION AND SUBTRACTION

EXTENSIONS
● Use three cards to generate three-digit numbers with two decimal places. Then ask: 'What do I need to add to get to the next tenth? To the next whole number?'. Be very clear about language when you start working to more than one decimal place. Although we read a decimal such as 3.96 as 'three ninety-six' in the context of *money*, it is incorrect in other contexts: 3.96 can be read as 'three point nine six' or 'three and ninety-six hundredths' – it is **not** 'three point ninety-six'.
● Use the three digits to make a number in the hundreds and ask: 'What should I add to make this up to the next hundred?' (734 + ? = 800).

HOW MANY WAYS?

†† *Whole class* ⏲ *10 minutes*

AIMS
To help the children develop strategies for addition (of two- and three-digit pairs). To look for numbers which together add up to a given total.

WHAT TO DO
Write up the following numbers on the board:

> 145, 124, 296, 94, 239, 363

Ask the children what number sentences they can make using these six numbers:

> (145 + 94 = 239, 239 + 124 = 363,
> 124 + 145 = 269 and so on)

DISCUSSION QUESTIONS
● *Did you estimate first?*
● *What calculations did you perform?*
● *If you are adding a number with 9 in the '1s' place what can you do to make things easier?* (round up to the nearest 10, calculate, subtract 1)
● *How can you make sure you don't lose track?*

VARIATION
To generate six interrelated numbers, choose the first few randomly and use them to generate the others: so a + b = c, c + d = e, a + d = f.

EXTENSIONS
● Use larger or smaller numbers as appropriate. (Y6/P7 might work with numbers around 500, for example. See page 18.)
● Split the numbers down further so that three are needed to make a total.

CAR BOOT SALE

†† *Whole class* ⏲ *10–15 minutes*

AIM
To consider strategies for the addition of money and giving change from £5.00.

WHAT TO DO
Write up a list like the one below:

CD	£2.85
Poster	£1.30
Box	£2.70
Jumper	£3.25
Books	35p each
Pack of ten old football programmes	£3.75

Tell the children they each have £5.00 to spend. Ask them what they could buy, how much it would cost and how much change they would be given.

DISCUSSION QUESTIONS
● *Do you add money in a different way from other numbers?*
● *What calculations do you perform to calculate the change?*
● *Which strategies are most effective?*

ASSESSMENT QUESTION
● *Amanda got 85p change when she bought two items. What were the two items?*
(poster and CD)

EXTENSIONS
● Allow £10.00 spending money.
● Make the items more expensive.

FAIRGROUND FUN

†† *Whole class*   ⏲ *10–20 minutes*

AIMS

To develop strategies for adding more than two numbers. To consider the properties of numbers.

WHAT TO DO

Copy the following diagram on to the board:

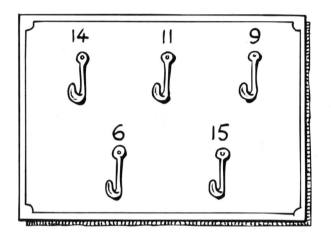

Tell the children that you have drawn a fairground game a bit like 'Hoopla'. Explain that you can throw up to three rings on to the hooks hung on the wall, but only one ring may hang on each hook. Pose some of the following problems:
- Paula got rings on 15 and 14. What was her score? (29)
- Roger scored 26. How might he have done that? (9, 6 and 11, or 15 and 11)
- Danielle missed the 11 and the 6 and scored on the others. What was her score? (38)
- Runa got the maximum possible score with her three rings. What was her score? (40)
- Michael only missed the 14 and 9 hooks. What did he score? (32)
- Paul scored three more than Harun, they both got the same number of rings on hooks. What did they each score? (6 vs 9; 11 and 15 vs 14 and 9; 6, 11 and 15 vs 6, 14 and 9)
- What is the difference between the maximum and minimum scores?
- You win a goldfish bowl for getting three rings on hooks and a final score that is an even number. With what scores will you win a goldfish bowl? (There is more than one possible answer to this. The different opinions should be discussed.)
- If only two rings stay on the board, is your score more likely to be odd or even? (odd)
- Which is greater: the maximum possible even total or the maximum possible odd total? (odd)

DISCUSSION QUESTIONS
- *What answer did you get? Does anyone disagree?*
- *How did you work that out? Did anyone do it differently?*

EXTENSIONS
- Challenge the children to find ways to make the game easier or harder.
- Follow up the mental maths session by writing up this work on the writing frame photocopiable sheet given on page 64.

JAM JAR SAVINGS

†† *Whole class*   ⏲ *10 minutes +*

AIM

To develop strategies for the addition of money and use of decimal notation.

YOU WILL NEED

One copy of photocopiable page 58 per child.

WHAT TO DO

Give each child a copy of the photocopiable sheet. Then explain to the class that Mrs S Avealot collects money in jars hidden around her house. She wants £10.00 to send to her niece for her birthday. From which jars could she make a total of exactly £10.00? (If she takes a jar out she always empties it!)

Ways of making exactly £10.00 include:
- £4.30, and £5.70;
- £5.90, £3.00, and £1.10.

A useful strategy is to pick a jar, perhaps £4.80, and ask: 'If she uses this jar, how much more money will she need? Is there a jar with that amount in? Are there two jars I can add together to give me that amount?'

DISCUSSION QUESTIONS
- *How did you calculate that?*
- *How much more will you need to add on to the money in this jar?*
- *Did you estimate first?*
- *How did you make your estimate?*
- *How many ways can she collect the £10?*

EXTENSION
- All the amounts in the jars are 'round' 10ps. Change the amounts so that this is no longer the case, including £2.54, 96p, and so on.

FENCE IT IN

†† *Any size* 🕐 *10–15 minutes*

AIM
To develop strategies for, and practise, the addition of decimals in the context of length.

WHAT TO DO
Write up the lengths of fencing (shown below) large enough for everyone to see:

> 10.70m, 5.90m, 13.20m, 12.90m, 18.20m, 4.40m, 7.50m, 8.10m, 2.60m, 1.20m, 6.70m

Tell the children that a farmer has been fencing in several of his fields and has lots of bits of off-cut fencing left over which he wants to use up. His last field is 20m long. Which of the pieces could he use to make the final length of fence?

DISCUSSION QUESTIONS
● *Will any combination of pieces fit exactly?* (10.70m + 8.10m + 1.20m)
● *Are there any others?*
● *Which other pieces could he use with the minimum of waste?*
● *How can you estimate the answer first?*
● *Does it help to look at the first digit?*

EXTENSIONS
● Make the lengths more precise by giving them to two decimal places, for example 10.73m.
● Mixing units makes the task very difficult (for example, 1.25m, 80cm, 2.05m and so on).

HOW MUCH MORE?

†† *Whole class* 🕐 *10 minutes*

AIMS
To decide on the mathematics needed to solve a problem. To discuss strategies for problem solving.

WHAT TO DO
Decide on a number type. For example:
● 1.20km and 0.80km (multiples of ten, same units);
● 1.20m and 80cm (multiples of ten, different units);
● 3kg and 2.8kg (same units, expressed with the minimum number of digits);
● 12.6m and 123cm (two- or three-digit numbers, different units).

Decide on a format such as:

$a + b = ?$	$a + ? = c$	$? + b = c$
$a - b = ?$	$a - ? = c$	$? - b = c$

Put the numbers, as measures, into a story, so if you have decided to use multiples of ten and different units you might say:

$a + b = ?$ A snail crawled 3.90m to reach a leaf, it then crawled to the end of the leaf. The leaf was 30cm long. How far had the snail crawled?

$a + ? = c$ At the start of his holiday Mr Scott's car had already travelled 2340 km. By the end of his holiday this had increased to 3600 km. How far had he driven?

$? + b = c$ Henry was given 3.50m of track for his model railway. He now has a total of 5.80m of track. How much did he have to start with?

$a - b = ?$ Mrs Lonsdale had a 240cm plank of wood. She used 1.30m to make a shelf. How much wood is left over?

$a - ? = c$ Mr Jandu bought 6kg of potatoes. He has got 4300g left. What weight of potatoes has he eaten?

$? - b = c$ Carol used string to tie a parcel. She used 70cm of string and now she has 2.70m left. How much did she have to start with?

DISCUSSION QUESTIONS
● *Is that a reasonable answer? How do you know?*
● *Can you explain what you need to do to solve the problem?*
● *How did you get that answer?*
● *Did anyone do it differently?*

ASSESSMENT QUESTIONS
● *Could you write a number sentence to express the mathematics?*
● *Would anyone write it differently?*

EXTENSION
Give 'longer' stories, such as: Ms Smith's journey to work is a complicated one. She walks 500m to the bus stop and rides the bus for 2.3km to the train station. She takes the train to the nearest town, 12km away. Then she takes another bus 4.7km into the town centre before walking the last 700m. How far does she travel every morning?

CONSECUTIVE PAIRS

†† *Individuals or pairs* ⏱ *About 45 minutes*

AIM
To consider the addition of consecutive numbers.

WHAT TO DO
Deal a card from a 0–100 pack and ask the children to work alone, or in pairs, to find out whether this number can be expressed as the sum of two consecutive numbers.

Note: any odd number can be expressed as the sum of two consecutive numbers. To find out what the consecutive numbers are, subtract 1 from the number, half the even number you get, and that number and the number plus 1 are the two consecutive numbers. *For example, 73 can be expressed as the sum of 36 + 37 (73 – 1 = 72, half of 72 is 36).*

DISCUSSION QUESTIONS
● *How would you set about investigating which numbers can be written as the sum of two consecutive numbers?*
● *What strategies can you use to find the consecutive numbers quickly?*

ASSESSMENT QUESTIONS
● *Can you make a general statement or write a rule to tell if a number can be made by adding two consecutive numbers?*
● *Can you make a general statement about the numbers which cannot be expressed as the sum of two consecutive numbers?*
● *Which two consecutive numbers can I subtract to give me an answer of 1?*
(any two)

EXTENSIONS
● Ask the children if the same rules hold true for numbers beyond 100? What about negative numbers?
● List the consecutive numbers 1, 2, 3, 4, ... 19, 20. Ask the children to circle three that add up to 39; 30; 24. Can they generalise a rule?
● Use the writing frame on photocopiable page 64 to reflect on and record the work done.

ADDITION OF FRACTIONS

†† *Individuals or pairs* ⏱ *20–30 minutes*

AIM
To develop strategies for the addition and subtraction of fractions.

WHAT TO DO
Ask the children how many different ways they can make a total of 1 with the addition of three fractions with the same denominator. Ask them to write ten examples, such as:

$$\frac{3}{10} + \frac{6}{10} + \frac{1}{10}$$

Note: There are an infinite number of possible solutions to this. If the children realise this then move on to the extension.

DISCUSSION QUESTIONS
● *If I start with $\frac{2}{7}$, how can I work out what I need to add to make 1?*
● *Who can come and write up one of his or her examples?*
● *Does everyone agree that these add up to 1?*
● *What did you use to help you devise this number sentence?*
● *Did anyone use a different piece of knowledge?*
● *Can anyone draw a diagram or a picture to demonstrate why this is right?*

ADDITION AND SUBTRACTION

ASSESSMENT QUESTIONS
● *What do I need to add to $\frac{13}{21}$ to get 1?*
● *If the probability of pulling a red sock out of a drawer is $\frac{3}{8}$, what is the probability of choosing a sock that isn't red?*
● *I have spent $\frac{4}{5}$ of my holiday money – how much is left?*

EXTENSIONS
● How many ways can the children find to add three fractions to make a total of 1 if all the fractions must have a different denominator? (In this case, they will need to use what they know about equivalence.)
● This activity can be written up on the writing frame photocopiable sheet given on page 64.

MINUS MINUS

✚✚ *Individuals, followed by whole-class discussion*
🕐 *20-minute investigation then 5-minute discussion*

AIM
To explore the addition and subtraction of negative numbers.

YOU WILL NEED
Calculators.

WHAT TO DO
Ask the children to investigate what happens when negative numbers are added or subtracted.

Encourage them to try adding and subtracting different pairs of negative numbers. Let them use calculators for this.

Discuss what they have noticed and ask them to try to generalise the results.

They should find that adding two negative numbers gives a 'bigger' negative number (although this, in fact, is a smaller number, further away from 0 on a number line: $-25 + -25 = -50$, $-50 < -25$). Subtracting one negative number from another means that they move along the number line towards, or even beyond 0, to a 'smaller' negative number or a positive number (for example, $-5 - -2 = -3$, $-5 - -5 = 0$, $-5 - -10 = 5$).

When modelling negative numbers we often use metaphors about lifts and ask children to imagine the lifts going below ground. Unfortunately this is rather a limited metaphor and is not helped by our habit of naming floors below ground as 'lower ground floor'. It is generally better to talk in terms of bank balances (for example, if I had £5 in my bank balance and took out £15, I would have –£10, so I would be in debt and owe the bank £10), or movement along a number line.

DISCUSSION QUESTIONS
● *How could we investigate this systematically?*
● *Can you show me what happens on the number line?*
● *Have you thought of all the possible combinations? How can you be sure?*

ASSESSMENT QUESTIONS
● *Do the rules that generally apply to addition and subtraction remain true when negative numbers are used? What changes (if anything)?*
● *What rules do we need to add to the ones we already know or how can we refine the rules we are already familiar with?*

EXTENSIONS
● Can you think of any real-life situations when the negative number calculations you have been working on would be appropriate? (temperature fluctuations, bank balances)
● Write a word problem to go with:

> a negative number + a negative number;
> a negative number – a negative number;
> a negative number + a positive number;
> a positive number + a negative number, etc

● What happens when you multiply and divide with negative numbers?
Note: The rule that if you multiply two negative numbers you get a positive number is a mathematical convention and has no other explanation.
● Can you derive general rules for these situations?
● Reflect upon and write up the work using the writing frame (photocopiable page 64).

TWO BY TWO

†† *Pairs or a small group*   ⏱ *20–30 minutes*

AIM
To practise addition of three two-digit numbers.

YOU WILL NEED
For each pair or group: two packs of 20–100 cards, a 10 × 10 grid as a base board filled in with random numbers between 40 and 200, a set of different-coloured counters for each child playing.

HOW TO PLAY
The cards are shuffled and each player is dealt three cards. The dealer then adds the numbers on his own three cards. If his total is on the board then he covers it with a counter and puts his cards in a discard pile. If the total is not on the board or is already covered, play passes to the next child.

Three new cards are dealt at the beginning of each turn and used cards are always placed on a discard pile. The first child to get four of her counters in a row wins (or whoever has the most counters on the board at the end of a set period of time).

If anyone has particular problems with specific aspects of the addition, for example crossing a decade (as in 27 + 36) you could remove cards with smaller '1s' digits so the children are more likely to have to practise this aspect of addition.

DISCUSSION QUESTIONS
● *What is the next number you need to make?*
● *Which cards would give that as a total?*
● *Which numbers are easiest to make? Why?*
● *Which numbers are hardest to make? Why?*

VARIATIONS
● Give a set time (perhaps 10 seconds) within which children must answer.
● Play collaboratively to see how many numbers can be covered in a given time.
● Allow subtraction to be used as well as addition.

EXTENSION
Use number cards over 100, decimals, money, weight or time. The baseboard will need to be redesigned in each case.

FOUR IN A LINE

†† *Two to four players*
⏱ *10–20 minutes per round*

AIM
To develop and practise strategies for the addition and subtraction of decimals.

YOU WILL NEED
For each group of players: a 0–10 number line marked in decimal tenths (ie 0, 0.1, 0.2 and so on), 100 cards numbered from 0–10, also in decimal tenths. Each player will also need a different-coloured felt-tipped pen.

HOW TO PLAY
Player 1 nominates a target number and draws a card from the pack. She should then state what she must add to or subtract from that number to reach her target and explain how she worked it out. For example, if the target number was 7.6, and a card with 2.8 on was drawn, then 4.8 would need to be added to make the target number.

If the other players agree, Player 1 can mark her target number on the number line (in this example, 7.6) and play moves on to the next person.

If another player does not agree, and can show Player 1 why she is wrong, then she misses her turn. However, if the challenge is incorrect she has another go.

The first person to get four marks on the number line in a consecutive row wins.

DISCUSSION QUESTIONS
● *How did you work out the difference between the numbers?*
● *Can you adapt the strategies you use with whole numbers to help you work out what you need to do?*
● *Are there some numbers that are easier to make than others?*
● *Are there any combinations of numbers you find particularly awkward to deal with?*
● *Is it possible to block your opponent?*

VARIATIONS
● A time limit may be placed on the thinking time each player is allowed.
● Disallow whole number targets.
● To make the game easier – play with ordinary 0–100 cards on a 0–100 number line.

EXTENSION
Play on a 0–1 number line or on a –50–50 number line marked in hundredths. In either case you will need to make cards to match.

STRATEGIES

CHILDREN SHOULD BE WORKING WITH NUMBERS OF THE ORDER:

YEAR 5/PRIMARY 6

● multiply and divide whole numbers by 10, 100, 1000;
● multiply two-digit numbers by a one-digit number;
● find unitary fractional quantities of numbers such as $\frac{1}{5}$ of 35;
● find simple percentages of quantities such as 10%, 20%, 25%, 50% and 75%;
● divide numbers based on their knowledge of multiplication facts, expressing any remainders as whole numbers or as fractions, such as $\frac{16}{7} = 2$ r2 (or $2\frac{2}{7}$) but $\frac{29}{3} = 9\frac{2}{3}$

YEAR 6/PRIMARY 7

● multiply or divide a two-digit number by a one-digit number such as 2.3 × 7 or 34 × 8;
● multiply or divide any whole number by a multiple of 10, 100, or 1000;
● multiply or divide decimals by 10, 100, or 1000 in the context of measures or money;
● calculate fractional quantities of numbers such as $\frac{3}{5}$ of 35;
● calculate percentages of quantities such as 15% of 500, 30% of 120;
● divide numbers based on knowledge of multiplication facts, either giving a remainder or (where straightforward) a fraction or decimal; $\frac{65}{7} = 9$ r2 (or $9\frac{2}{7}$)
but $\frac{29}{3} = 9\frac{2}{3} = 9.66$ and $\frac{17}{4} = 4.25$

AS A MINIMUM, BY THE END OF YEAR 6/PRIMARY 7, MOST CHILDREN SHOULD:

● know and use multiplication and division facts to 10 x 10;
● know and use doubles of numbers to 50, then 100 and their corresponding halves.

Children will already have a range of mental strategies for multiplication and division. These need to be developed so that they become increasingly efficient and effective. Many things can slow children down and stop them developing better methods. The single most significant is a lack of known facts to draw upon.

With regard to division in the context of problems, pupils will need to learn to make decisions about the degree of accuracy required and the appropriate form for remainders. For example, $\frac{19}{4}$ gives an answer of $4\frac{3}{4}$ or 4.75; in the context of money the decimal representation is more appropriate, but in the context of sharing slices of toast, say, the fraction might seem more appropriate. If the question relates to a non-divisible unit, rounding may be necessary.

(For example, 19 people decide to go to the theatre and want to go in minicabs. Four people can go in each minicab. How many cabs do they need to call?)

When multiplying and dividing, numbers can quickly become too large to manage mentally. Paper and pencil may be required to 'extend the mental screen' and to hold numbers that represent steps on the way to an answer. For example, if you were to calculate 15% of 230, you may want to jot down 11.5 as 5% of 230 before adding the 11.5 to the 23 mentally.

Examples are given below to show how the children may develop and adapt and add to their strategies as they mature.

STRATEGIES FOR MULTIPLICATION

Shift to the left to multiply by 10, 100, or 1000 uses knowledge that multiplying by powers of 10 shifts the number to the left in relation to the decimal point:

> in Y5/P6 a child might solve:
> 23 × 100 by shifting two places to the left
> 23.000 to 2300.0

> in Y6/P7 a child might convert:
> 23m to 2300cm by shifting two places to the left of the decimal point

For multiples of 10, 100, or 1000 the older (Y6/P7) or more able child may use the knowledge that multiplying by powers of 10 shifts the number to the left in relation to the decimal point together with memorised multiplication facts:

> 35 × 300 → 35 × 3 × 100
> 4.7 × 20 → 4.7 × 2 × 10

Partitioning when multiplying a two-digit number by a one-digit number shows that the child understands that numbers can be partitioned into parts for multiplication:

> in Y5/P6 a child might solve:
> 37 × 6 → (30 × 6) + (7 × 6)

> in Y6/P7 a child might solve:
> 37 × 16 → (37 × 10) + (30 × 6) + (7 × 6)

Using multiplication facts flexibly: compensation

in Y5/P6 a child might solve:
$34 \times 9 \rightarrow (34 \times 10) - 34$

in addition in Y6/P7 a child might solve:
$34 \times 11 \rightarrow (34 \times 10) + 34$

Using multiplication facts flexibly: uses doubling

in Y5/P6 a child might solve:
$43 \times 4 \rightarrow (43 \times 2) \times 2$ or double (43×2)
$35 \times 8 \rightarrow [(35 \times 2) \times 2] \times 2$ or double double (43×2)

in addition in Y6/P7 a child might solve:
$17 \times 40 \rightarrow [(17 \times 2) \times 2] \times 10$ or [double double $(17 \times 2)] \times 10$

Using pencil and paper: While an older (Y6/P7) or more able child will continue to use mental strategies at some point these will need to be extended with paper and pencil for numbers too large to hold mentally.

Extending the doubling strategy with some recording:

$24 \times 13 \rightarrow$
$1 \times 24 = 24$
$2 \times \quad = 48$
$4 \times \quad = 96$
$8 \times \quad = 192$

since:
$13 = 8 + 4 + 1$, 24×13 is $192 + 96 + 24 = 312$

Extending the partitioning strategy with some recording when multiplying a two-digit number by a two-digit number:

$17 \times 24 \rightarrow$

	10	+	7	
20	200		140	= 340
+				
4	40		28	= 68
				= 408

STRATEGIES FOR DIVISION

Using knowledge of multiplication facts:

the child reasons that it will take seven weeks to save up £40 at the rate of £6 per week because $6 \times 7 = 42$
and also solves $560 \div 8 = 70$ because $7 \times 8 = 56$

To divide by 10, 100, or 1000 the child may use the knowledge that to divide by a power of 10 numbers shift to the right in relation to the decimal point:

$34 \div 10 = 3.4$ converts 345m into km by shifting to the right: $345/1000 = 0.345$km

Doubling and halving may be combined, so a child may divide by 5 by dividing by 10 and doubling the tenth:

$48 \div 5 \rightarrow (48 \div 10) \times 2$

Or the child may use repeated halving to divide by 2, 4 and 8:

$140 \div 4 \rightarrow (140 \div 2)/2$

Converts simple percentages such as 33%, 25%, 50%, 66% and 75% into fractions for calculation:

33% of £270 $\rightarrow \frac{1}{3} \times 270 = 90$

Calculates complex percentages as compounds:

$15\% \rightarrow 10\% + 5\%$

VAT at 17.5% can be calculated as 10% + 5% + 2.5%, each stage is found by halving the one before:

$30\% \rightarrow$ either $3 \times 10\%$
or $(2 \times 10\%) + 10\%$

MULTIPLICATION AND DIVISION

RAPID RECALL

⊓⊓ *Whole class, then individuals*
🕐 *5–10 minutes with the whole class, then about 10 minutes per person*

AIMS
To help children identify the multiplication facts they do not know so that they can target their efforts to learn these. To reinforce the link between multiplication and division.

YOU WILL NEED
A large multiplication square big enough for everyone to see, a marker pen, one copy of photocopiable page 59 for each pair of children.

WHAT TO DO
Discuss the other related things that you know if you are already aware that $3 \times 6 = 18$ ($6 \times 3 = 18$, $18 \div 3 = 6$, $18 \div 6 = 3$). Draw attention to the multiplication grid and ask if anyone has ever noticed anything about it. If nobody mentions it, point out the symmetry brought about because $3 \times 4 = 4 \times 3$ and $8 \times 6 = 6 \times 8$.

Ask if anyone knows what is special about the line of symmetry. (It is formed by the square numbers, the point where each number is multiplied by itself.)

Once you have established that you do not need to learn all the multiplication facts as half of it repeats the other half, use a marker pen to cross out half the multiplication facts (always an enjoyable and liberating moment!).

Explain that you will gradually work your way around the class to check which facts people need to learn.

The language associated with the recall of multiplication (and division) facts needs to be varied. Here is a selection you might like to choose from:

Seven nines?	Four times three?
8 multiplied by 2?	Multiply 3 by 9.
How many 7s in 56?	Divide 45 by 9.
9 divided by 6?	6 divided by 9?
$\frac{1}{10}$ th of 20?	Divide 8 into 48.
What is 72 shared between 8?	

DISCUSSION QUESTIONS
● *Who can tell me about the two halves of the multiplication grid?*
● *Who can explain why they are the same?*
● *When you are trying to learn your multiplication facts do you need to learn all of them?*

ASSESSMENT
Prepare and cut up sufficient copies of photocopiable page 59 to allow one grid per child. Sit down with a child and tell him that you are going to test his ability to recall multiplication facts. All facts that are known will be entered on the grid as a tick; facts that he needs to work out (where the recall is too slow) will be written in blue, and any facts that he doesn't know will be written in green. Ask random multiplication facts, but be careful only to fill in responses on half of the grid. Start with a few easy ones, then mix up the easy and the more difficult.

A completed grid might look like the one below. This gives the children a very clear idea of what they don't know and a clear set of targets to aim for (rather than a general comment about needing to learn their tables!).

1	2	3	4	5	6	7	8	9	10
2	✓								
3	✓	✓							
4	✓	✓	✓						
5	✓	✓	✓	✓					
6	✓	✓	✓	✓	✓				
7	✓	✓	28	✓	42	49			
8	✓	✓	✓	✓	48	56	✓		
9	✓	✓	36	✓	54	63	✓	✓	
10	✓	✓	✓	✓	✓	✓	✓	✓	100

Look across all the multiplication grids as you complete them. If there are facts unknown by large numbers of children in the class a 'fact of the day' can be useful. This should be repeated by as many people as often as possible – one by one as they go out to play, before you will answer a question, every time the hamster puts in an appearance and so on.

DOUBLING

♦♦ *Whole class* ⏰ *10–15 minutes*

AIM
To extend the children's awareness of the potential uses for doubling strategies.

WHAT TO DO
Tell the children that you are going to see what use they can make of their ability to double numbers.

First of all ask them what they can tell you about ways to double numbers or what it means to double a number (either multiplying by two or adding a number to itself).

Choose a number to double, say 13. Write up on the board:

$$1 \times 13 = 13$$

Then ask them what 2×13 is. Write this below the first multiple:

$$1 \times 13 = 13$$
$$2 \times 13 = 26$$

Now ask what happens if you double 26, write the answer in:

$$2 \times 26 = 52$$

Then ask how many 13s you now have and add this number sentence:

$$4 \times 13 = 52$$
$$8 \times 13 = 104$$

Go on to ask what 8×13 would be:

$$8 \times 13 = 104$$

Continue for as long as you like.

Try a different number. Emphasise the fact that as you double the total, so you are also doubling the number of 'lots of' the original number.

DISCUSSION QUESTIONS
● *How many 'lots of' this have we got now? How do you know?*
● *What happens if we start off multiplying by three and then double? And double again?*
(6×, 12× and so on)

ASSESSMENT QUESTIONS
● *How could I multiply 17 by 8? Or 83 by 4?*
● *How could I use doubling to multiply 30 by 24?*
(×3, ×2, ×2, ×2)
● *How could I use doubling to solve 12×18?*
($12 \times 9 \times 2$ and so on)

EXTENSIONS
● Tell the children that some people use doubling for a lot of their multiplication needs. Could they use it to solve 11×17?

$$1 \times 17 = 17$$
$$2 \times 17 = 34$$
$$4 \times 17 = 68$$
$$8 \times 17 = 136$$

($8 + 2 + 1 = 11$, so add $136 + 34 + 17 = 187$)

● Use doubling to multiply decimal quantities such as 3.4×8.
● You should bring it to the children's attention that ultimately doubling is not always an effective strategy (468×973?), but it is very useful for mental work with relatively low numbers.

HALVING

♦♦ *Whole class* ⏰ *10–15 minutes*

AIM
To extend the children's awareness of the potential uses for halving strategies.

WHAT TO DO
Tell the children that you want to see what uses they can make of their ability to halve numbers.

Elicit some strategies for halving numbers to 100 for both even and odd numbers.

Ask the children what happens if they halve an odd number.

Then ask them what happens if they halve a number and then halve it again? ($\frac{1}{4}$) ... and half it again? ($\frac{1}{8}$) And again? ($\frac{1}{16}$) And so on.

Try it with a large number recording as in 'Doubling' on this page.

DEVELOPING MENTAL MATHS

MULTIPLICATION AND DIVISION

MULTIPLICATION AND DIVISION

DISCUSSION QUESTIONS
- *How could I divide a number by 4? Or 8?*
- *Can you use the halving strategy to calculate $\frac{1}{8} \times 820$? What stages would you go through?*
- *Could you use halving to help you find $\frac{1}{16}$ or $\frac{1}{12}$ of 216? Does it help to know that $\frac{1}{3}$ of 216 is 72?*

ASSESSMENT QUESTIONS
- *What happens when you quarter 95? How can you tackle this?*
- *Has anyone in the class found a different way to deal with this problem? Which method do you think is most efficient?*

As all the problems above feature purely numerical calculations, you could ask children to tackle word problems such as: 'If 16 people share an inheritance of £32 000, how much does each person receive?'

EXTENSION
Ask the children to try using halving to divide fractional quantities such as $28.8 \div 4$ or $\frac{1}{2}$ of $\frac{3}{4}$.

MULTIPLY IT OUT

✝✝ Whole class
🕐 *10–15 minutes repeated regularly throughout blocks of work on multiplication*

AIM
To facilitate a discussion of multiplication strategies.

WHAT TO DO
When choosing the numbers for this activity, you need to establish a progression, from working with multiplication facts the children already know, to dealing with:
- two-digit multiples of 10, or three-digit multiples of 100, multiplied by a single digit (60×8, 400×9, $20 \times ? = 180$, $? \times 7 = 210$);
- any two-digit number multiplied by a one-digit number (32×4, 52×6, $53 \times ? = 159$, $? \times 4 = 56$);
- a decimal such as 0.3 multiplied by a one-digit number (0.3×3, 0.4×7, $0.6 \times ? = 1.8$, $? \times 4 = 24.8$);
- a decimal such as 2.6 multiplied by a one-digit number (8.2×3, 8.3×6, $2.4 \times ? = 7.2$).

Prepare three or four appropriate questions (such as those above) to use to elicit strategies. Be wary of explanations such as 'I did 0.3×3 by doing 3×3 and then put the point back'. Although you may know what is meant it may cause confusion for other children. To think of 0.3 as 3 you have to multiply it by 10. This means you will have to divide by 10 at the end to undo the adjustment you made.

DISCUSSION QUESTIONS
The generic questions on page 9 are a good place to start the discussion.
- *How can you use what you know about multiplication to solve this problem?*
- *Did anyone split the numbers up?* (partitioning, or using the Distributive Law, can be a useful strategy in such problems)
- *Did you have to multiply or divide by 10 at the end?*

ASSESSMENT QUESTION
What is the area of a rectangle with sides of 1.2m and 60cm?
($7200cm^2$ or $0.72m^2$)

EXTENSIONS
- To consolidate new knowledge ask the children to work through a set of similar written examples mentally, writing down how they found each answer.
- Encourage the children to write up their thoughts on the writing frame photocopiable sheet given on page 64.

MULTIPLYING & DIVIDING BY POWERS OF 10

✝✝ Whole class · 🕐 *10–15 minutes*

AIM
To generalise the effect of multiplying and dividing by powers of 10.

WHAT TO DO
Ask the children what happens if a number is multiplied by 10 or by 100. Ask for examples and write these up so that everyone can see them.

Beware of the rule that says 'To multiply by 10, add a 0', this is fine for whole numbers but can cause problems with products such as 3.4×10; if children overapply the rule they will answer this as 3.40. It is less likely to cause confusion if you talk in terms of numbers moving to the left of the decimal place. So for example 34.0 becomes 340 and 5.7 becomes 57. In division the numbers move to the right. You need to be clear that this only happens when you multiply (or divide) by whole numbers – consider what happens if you multiply 0.3 by 0.1.

Children will need to become familiar with the effects of multiplying and dividing whole and decimal numbers by multiples of 10. Consider as starting points:

> a three-digit number multiplied by 10 or 100
> (326 × 10, 473 × 100, 232 × ? = 23200)
>
> a three-digit multiple of 10 or 100 divided by 10 or 100
> (340 ÷ 10, 6700 ÷ 100, 230 ÷ ? = 23)
>
> multiplying two multiples of 10
> (30 × 40, 20 × 150, 70 × ? = 4900)
>
> dividing two- or three-digit numbers by 10 or 100 (68 ÷ 10, 673 ÷ 100, ? ÷ 10 = 43.2, 291 ÷ ? = 2.91)
>
> multiplying decimal numbers by 10 or 100 (0.4 × 10, 2.3 × 10, 2.3 × 100, 0.23 × 100, and so on)

Work together to consider what happens in each case. You may want to allow the children access to calculators for a short while at the start of this activity if they find it difficult to generate ideas as a prelude to generating rules.

DISCUSSION QUESTIONS
● *What is happening?*
● *Is that statement precise enough?*
● *What would happen if...?*
● *Can we generalise a rule?*
● *How can we describe the circumstances in which our rule works?*
● *Can we adapt a rule we wrote before?*

ASSESSMENT QUESTIONS
● *There are 100cm in 1m – so how many metres in 320cm?*
● *How many centimetres in 5.6m?*
● *How many millimetres in 34cm?*
● *How many centimetres in 345mm?*

EXTENSIONS
● In each case move on from multiplying by 10 and 100, to multiplying by multiples of 10 and 100 (20, 30, 200, 300, and so on).
● Ask the children whether the rules they have generated apply to multiplying (or dividing) by 1000 or 10 000, or 100 000?
● This activity could be written up using the writing on the photocopiable sheet given on page 64.
● See also 'Function machines' on this page.

FUNCTION MACHINES

†† *Whole class* ⏲ *5–10 minutes*

AIM
To consider what happens when you multiply and divide by powers of 10.

WHAT TO DO
On the board draw a function machine like the one below:

Number in → ×10 → ×100 → ÷10 → Number out

The functions used should be either multiplying or dividing by multiples of 10. Decide on a number to put in (from the range suggested in 'Multiplying and dividing by powers of 10', on page 32) and ask the children to tell you what will come out at each stage. Repeat this three or four times.

DISCUSSION QUESTIONS
● *What is the overall effect of the machine?*
● *How do you know?*
● *Can you explain how you can work out the overall effect of the machine?*

ASSESSMENT QUESTIONS
● *The number that came out was 34, what number did I put in?*
● *The number out this time was 830, what number did I put in?*

EXTENSION
Use multiples of 10 and 100.

FRACTIONAL QUANTITIES

†† *Whole class* ⏲ *10–15 minutes*

AIM
To develop strategies for finding fractions of quantities and to reinforce the link between fractions and division.

WHAT TO DO
Children should start by working with unitary fractions where the numerator is 1 and the denominator is a number with whose multiples they are familiar (such as $\frac{1}{3}$, $\frac{1}{5}$ or $\frac{1}{9}$).

In this way they can use their knowledge of multiplication to support the division, so $\frac{1}{5}$ of 35 = 35 ÷ 5 = 7, for example. They can then move on to fractions where the numerator is any number smaller than the denominator (such as $\frac{2}{3}$, $\frac{3}{5}$ or $\frac{7}{9}$). In either case the fractional quantities used should provide whole number answers ($\frac{1}{5}$ of 65 is 13) as well as answers which are not whole numbers ($\frac{1}{6}$ of 20 is $3\frac{1}{3}$).

Devise some appropriate questions based on the information above. For example, if you are just starting this work with Year 5 you might ask: 'How can I find $\frac{1}{7}$ of 77? $\frac{1}{3}$ of 240?'

Children will also need experience of constructing fractions and learning how to simplify them: 'What fraction of a day is 1 hour? 8 hours? 12 hours? 24 hours?'

If children become proficient with these types of problem they may like to go on to consider improper (top heavy) fractions ($\frac{3}{2}$ of 40 is 60) or fractions with more complex denominators (such as $\frac{1}{20}$ or $\frac{1}{15}$).

DISCUSSION QUESTIONS
● *Can you describe the problem using other language?*
(as division for example)
● *What operation are you using?*
● *What facts that you know are you using?*
● *How can you check your answers?*
● *Would it help to estimate first?*
● *Can we write $\frac{8}{24}$ in another way?*
● *Can anyone think of some fractions that are equivalent to...?*

ASSESSMENT QUESTIONS
Try turning the structure of the problem around... rather than giving the starting numbers to find an answer, give an answer to work back from:
● *I spent $\frac{1}{5}$ of my holiday money on my first day at the seaside. I've got £20 left. How much did I have to start with?*
● *I ate $\frac{3}{4}$ of a box of chocolates. There are eight chocolates left in the box, how many did I eat?*

EXTENSIONS
● The writing frame photocopiable sheet on page 64 could be used to write up this work.
● Draw this pie chart where everyone can see it. For your information: bananas take up $\frac{1}{3}$, apples $\frac{1}{4}$, oranges and strawberries $\frac{1}{6}$ each and pineapple $\frac{1}{12}$. Tell the class that it shows the results of a survey conducted in a school of 480 pupils to find out their favourite fruit.

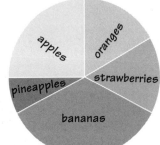

Ask questions such as:
● What fraction of the children prefer... ?
● How many children prefer... ?
and so on.
Note: Children should be able to relate fractions, decimals and percentages and use this knowledge when solving problems such as these.

SEVEN AND A BIT

†† *Whole class* ⏲ *10–15 minutes*

AIM
To consider the use of quotient and remainder in division.

WHAT TO DO
First, ask the children:
'If I wanted to put six sweets into each of some party bags and I had 63 sweets, how many party bags could I fill?' (10 r3). Elicit the children's strategies for working out the problem and ask for some suggestions of how it might be written as a mathematical sentence (either 63 – 6 – 6 – 6 – 6 – 6 – 6 – 6 – 6 – 6 – 6 = 3, or $\frac{63}{6}$ = 10 r3).

Then ask: 'If three people have to share ten pieces of toast, how many pieces of toast could each person have?' ($3\frac{1}{3}$). Again, elicit strategies and encourage the children to come up with a mathematical sentence you can write down (for example $\frac{10}{3} = 3\frac{1}{3}$).

Ask the children if they can see any difference between these two situations.

Talk about the fact that when you are sharing it is sensible to cut up something like a slice of toast, but that it is not possible to cut up or share out everything – it would not have been sensible to talk about 'half a party bag', nor fair to give one person only three sweets.

Explain that when the answer to a division is given as a whole number with something left over the mathematical terms for these are the **quotient** and the **remainder**.

Go on to ask how you might work out the remainders in the following calculations, if you wanted the answer in the form of a quotient and a remainder:

50/7   38/5   170/20   26/4   66/8   190/3

DISCUSSION QUESTIONS
● *How did you calculate that?*
● *What did you look at first? What did you say to yourself?*
● *Did anyone have a different method?*
● *Did you estimate first?*
● *Did you need to run right through your multiplication facts or could you see the answer quite quickly?*

ASSESSMENT QUESTIONS
As all the discussion questions were out of context and took the form a/b = quotient and remainder, where the answer comes at the end of the number sentence, put assessment questions into a context and make the unknown quantity come at a different point in the question. For example:
● *Eggs are packed into boxes of six. The farmer has filled five boxes with three eggs left over. How many eggs did he have to start with? (?/6 = 5 r3)*
● *A baker decided to sell iced buns in family packs. He had 59 buns to start with and he made seven family packs which left him with three individual buns. How many buns went into each family pack? (59/? = 7 r3)*

EXTENSIONS
● Try the game 'Quotient and remainder', given on page 43.
● Encourage the children to reflect and write up this work using the writing frame given on the photocopiable sheet on page 64.

CALCULATING PERCENTAGES

†† *Whole class*   ⏲ *10–15 minutes*

AIM
To develop strategies for calculating percentages of quantities.

WHAT TO DO
Children need to become familiar, initially, with calculating 10%, 25% and 50% of quantities and then to use this ability to calculate 5%, 15%, 20%, 30%, and 75%. It would also be useful for them to be able to calculate any percentage that is a multiple of 5 or 10 as well as the rate of VAT,

currently at 17.5%. This can be found by adding 10%, 5% and 2.5% – each quantity derived by halving the previous one.

With this in mind, choose percentages and quantities that will help the children to develop their own strategies. If they are already confident in finding 10% of a quantity, then move on to 15% or 20%: 'How can I calculate 10% of 360?'; 'If 10% of 360 is 36, then how could I calculate 5%?'
Note: Children should be encouraged to relate percentages to fractions and use this when solving problems relating to, for example, 25% ($\frac{1}{4}$), 50% ($\frac{1}{2}$) and 33% ($\frac{1}{3}$).

DISCUSSION QUESTIONS
● *How do we write 'ten percent'?*
● *Who can write 10% in a different way?*
($\frac{10}{100} = \frac{1}{10}$)
● *Can anyone explain what 'per cent' means?*
● *You divided by 10 to find 10% of 360. Why does that work?*
● *If you can work out 10% of a quantity, what else can you calculate easily?*
(5%, 20% and so on)
● *How will you calculate those other quantities?*

ASSESSMENT QUESTIONS
● *Do you know what 10% of 260 is?*
● *What about 5% or 15% of 260?*
(26, 13, 39)
● *Can you find 20% of 75?*
($2 \times 7.5 = 15$)
● *Now try 70% of 30?*
($7 \times 3 = 21$)
● *Before I went on holiday I bought a jacket. It cost £100. When I got back the price had gone up to £110. What was the percentage increase?*

EXTENSIONS
Challenge the children with problems on percentage increases or decreases such as:
● *My shoes cost £45.00, but were in the sale at 10% discount. How much did I pay?*
● *A scientist was measuring the growth of bamboo. In five days it increased its height by 30%. If it was 130cm tall on Monday, what was its height by Friday? (169cm)*
● See also: 'Price change' and 'Shop 'til you drop' on pages 49 and 56.

THE CONCERT IN THE PARK

†† *Any number to whole class*
🕐 *One lesson*

AIMS

To develop the use of division and multiplication to factorise numbers. To consider sensible answers within a context.

WHAT TO DO

Set the scene with the children. Tell them to imagine that the local authorities are holding a concert of classical music in a park next weekend. There will be seating arranged for people who wish to pay for it. The person arranging the chairs has been told to expect 210 people. Ask the children if they can work out how many different ways she could arrange the chairs into rows and columns.

DISCUSSION QUESTIONS

Imagine first of all that she is going to use rows and columns of the same length so that she puts out a rectangular array
● *In how many ways could she arrange the chairs?*
● *Which of these are suitable for a concert?*

EXTENSIONS

● The park attendant is cautious and decides that it would be sensible to plan on an extra 15% of people turning up.
● How many chairs will she use now?
● How should these be arranged? Will there be some 'part' rows?

● What if she decides on other arrays (perhaps triangular)?
● How much money will be raised if the average seat price is £5 and all the seats are sold (for both numbers of seats)?

BOXES OF BISCUITS

†† *Whole class, or groups of any size*
🕐 *15 minutes – one lesson*

AIM

To practise multiplying and dividing numbers by single digits and multiples of 10 in context.

WHAT TO DO

Set the scene by telling the children that Ms Nibbler makes handmade biscuits for the rich and famous. She, and her bakers, sell biscuits in boxes to expensive London shops. Each box holds 20 packets of biscuits and each packet holds nine biscuits. It takes them three hours to make enough biscuits to fill one box.

Then ask some (or all) of the following questions:
● What is the average time it takes to make one biscuit? (1 minute)
● How many boxes can be filled with 780 packets? (39)
● How many packets can be filled with 999 biscuits? (111)
● The Queen orders six packets. How long will it take to make the biscuits specially for her? (54 minutes)

Now tell the children that Ms Nibbler and her staff work from 9am to 4pm five days a week and they all take an hour for lunch.
● How many boxes of biscuits can they make in a day? A week? (2, 10)
● If they made 540 biscuits, how could I calculate how they would be packaged? (÷9, ÷20)

DISCUSSION QUESTIONS

● *How can you best estimate the answers?*
● *Would you calculate this differently if you were using a calculator? How?*
● *What steps are you using mentally? Could you approach the problem in a different way?*

EXTENSIONS

● How would they package 1620 biscuits? Can you work this out mentally?
● The numbers above can be changed to fit in with the size of numbers appropriate for groups or individuals by consulting the 'Children should be working with numbers of the order' section of page 28.

IN MY LIFE

†† *Whole class, then individuals*
🕐 *5–10 minutes discussion, then 20 minutes individual*

AIM
To use multiplication and division to solve problems involving large numbers.

WHAT TO DO
Ask a few children how old they are, possibly choosing one child who has just turned 11 and another who has been 11 for some time. Discuss the degree of accuracy we usually accept when we discuss ages. Ask how much time people spend each day on various activities such as sleeping, eating, reading or brushing their teeth. Suggest that the amount of time spent reading or sleeping, for example, might vary with age – children do not read at all until they are five or six, as they get older they read more, and if they go to university they may have to read a lot. Discuss the upper and lower limits for sensible estimates (for example, people are usually said to sleep for an average of eight hours a day).

Ask the children to make a calculated estimate of the number of hours they have spent sleeping or brushing their teeth.

DISCUSSION QUESTIONS
● *Before you try to calculate the answer – who can write a number sentence to show what they will need to work out?*
● *How accurate will your answer need to be?*
● *Will you need a calculator or can you round the numbers sufficiently to be able to do the calculations yourself?*
● *Will everyone's answer be the same? What factors will make answers difficult?*
(variations in estimating and rounding)

EXTENSIONS
● Paul's grandmother says that she has spent 10 000 hours brushing her teeth. Is this reasonable? What calculations would you need to do?
● If, at the age of 80, you had spent 10 000 hours

brushing your teeth, how many minutes would you have spent each day? (about 20)
● Children should write up their findings on the writing frame photocopiable sheet on page 64.

WHEELING ROUND

†† *Whole class then individuals*
🕐 *5–10 minutes discussion then 20 minutes individual*

AIM
To use multiplication and division to solve problems of ratio.

WHAT TO DO
Copy this drawing on to the board. Explain that if wheel A goes round once, wheel B goes round four times.

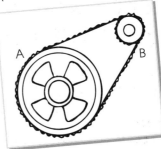

● If A goes round 20 times, how many times does B go round? If B goes round 160 times, how many times will A go round?
● The wheels are adjusted so that every time A goes round once, B goes round three times. If A goes round 17 times, how many times does B go round then? If B goes round 270 times, how many times will A go round?
● Every time A goes round *twice*, B goes round five times. If A goes round 120 times, how many times does B go round? (300) If B goes round 90 times, how many times will A go round? (36)

DISCUSSION QUESTIONS
● *What is the ratio of turns on the big wheel (A) to turns on the small wheel (B)?*
(1:4, 1:3, 2:5)
● *What maths did you do to work that out?*
● *If the big wheel goes round 75 times for every 150 the little wheel goes round, what is the ratio of turns on the big wheel to turns on the little wheel?*
● *How do you know?*
● *What is the shortest (most concise) way to express the ratio?*
(1:2)

EXTENSION
Ask the class to find out where else they might see ratios. (Scales on maps, scale models and so on.) Note some examples and encourage the children to describe what they mean.

DEVELOPING MENTAL MATHS

MULTIPLICATION AND DIVISION

MULTIPLICATION AND DIVISION

TWICE AS BIG

†† *Individuals, pairs or small groups.*
🕐 *About 45 minutes*

AIM
To consider what happens to area and volume when you make two- and three-dimensional shapes 'twice as big'.

YOU WILL NEED
Interlocking cubes.

WHAT TO DO
This activity explores applied number. Ask the children to make a rectangle with interlocking cubes. Then, without destroying the first rectangle, make another one twice as big.

DISCUSSION QUESTIONS
● *What is the area of the first rectangle?*
● *What do we mean by 'twice as big' – do you just need to double the length? What other dimensions need to be doubled?(Doubling the depth is at your discretion at this point, but perhaps is better left until later – see 'Extensions'.)*
● *What is the area of the second rectangle? Is it twice as big?*
● *How much bigger is the second rectangle?*
● *Is this always the case?*
● *What happens if you double the size of a triangle?*
● *And other shapes?*

ASSESSMENT QUESTIONS
● *Can you generalise a rule?*
● *How did you come to that decision?*
● *How specific does your rule need to be?*
● *What else could you investigate?*

EXTENSIONS
● Ask the children to make a three-dimensional object using the interlocking cubes and then ask them the same questions.
● Encourage the children to write up their findings on the writing frame on photocopiable page 64.

PRIME SIEVE

†† *Individuals, pairs, or small groups working collaboratively*
🕐 *20–30 minutes*

AIM
To help children understand (and begin to learn) the prime numbers < 100.

YOU WILL NEED
For each child or group: a set of 0–100 cards, a large sheet of paper marked with this grid big enough for 0–100 cards to be piled up on the numbers:

2	3	4	5
6	7	8	9

WHAT TO DO
Consider each 0–100 card in turn. Decide which of the numbers 2–9 are a factor of the number on the card, place the card on that number and go on to the next card. (A number cannot be placed upon itself, so the 3 card cannot be put on the 3, while the 9 card cannot be put on the 9, but can be put on the 3.) Point out that 1 is not included on the grid. Children will be aware that some numbers have more than one factor and that it does not matter which number they place it on – they should decide. Numbers about which they are unsure or which they cannot place should be put to one side to be considered more carefully on a second sort. A final check should leave the children with a pile of cards which have no factors other than 1 and themselves – these are the prime numbers.

The prime numbers less than 100 are: 2, 3, 5, 7, 11, 13, 17, 19, 23, 29, 31, 37, 41, 43, 47, 53, 59, 61, 67, 71, 73, 79, 83, 89 and 97.

SOME STRATEGIES FOR TESTING DIVISIBILITY OR FACTORISING A NUMBER
Go to the nearest known multiple or the tenth multiple. For example:
● Is 48 divisible by 7?
It can't be because $7 \times 7 = 49$
● Is 97 divisible by 7?
$10 \times 7 = 70$ which is 27 away from 97 and 27 is not divisible by 7 so neither is 97
● Is 51 divisible by 3?
$51 = 30 + 21$ both of which are divisible by 3 so 3 is a factor and so is 17 ($\frac{30}{3} = 10 + \frac{21}{3}$)

For large numbers and finding factors by trial and improvement, as all factors come in pairs you can stop testing at the square root of the number. For example, $\sqrt{1997} = 44.69$ so one of each pair of factors will be less than 44.

DISCUSSION QUESTIONS

● *How can you be sure that this number has no factors (other than 1 and itself)?*
● *Can you write a general statement about the numbers that will not fit on your grid?*
● *Can you write a definition for a prime number?*
● *Are there any groups of numbers you know will not be prime?*
(ie, all even numbers and numbers ending in a 5)

ASSESSMENT QUESTION

How can you work out which factors a particular number has?

EXTENSIONS

● Ask the children to factorise the numbers fully and record all the factors on paper. See below for some strategies for factorising.
● Investigate numbers over 100 – is 1997 a prime number?
● Encourage the children to write up their findings on the writing frame photocopiable sheet given on page 64.
● See also the activity 'Prime factors' on this page.

WRITING PAPER

†† *Individuals or pairs*   ⏱ *About 45 minutes*

AIM

To explore how factorising numbers can be used to solve problems.

WHAT TO DO

Describe the following problem to the children.
● The area of a rectangular sheet of writing paper is 420cm². What are the possible dimensions for the sheet, if all measurements must be in whole centimetres? (1 × 420, 2 × 210, 3 × 140, 4 × 104, 5 × 84, 6 × 70, 10 × 42, 12 × 35, 15 × 28, 20 × 21, 30 × 14, 70 × 6.)

DISCUSSION QUESTIONS

● *How can you approach the problem methodically?*
● *Which of the dimensions would be most sensible?*
● *Have you thought of all the possible dimensions? How do you know?*

ASSESSMENT QUESTIONS

● *What knowledge were you using to help you?*
● *How do you know when to stop looking for further dimensions?*

EXTENSIONS

● Write up the work on the writing frame photocopiable page 64.
● Modify the numbers involved. You could make the surface area larger (perhaps for a sheet of wrapping paper) or allow parts of centimetres in the dimensions. You could also specify the ground floor area of a flat and ask what possible dimensions it might have or what dimensions are possible if the flat is L-shaped.
(Some estate agents have floor plans available for potential purchasers which might be interesting to look at.)

PRIME FACTORS

†† *Individuals or small groups*
⏱ *About 45 minutes*

AIMS

To explore prime factors. To investigate the potential for expressing any number as the product of its prime factors.

WHAT TO DO

Discuss with the children what a prime number is. (If they do not know then they could work through 'Prime sieve' on page 38.) Ask them what the

factors of 12 are (1, 2, 3, 4, 6, 12) and see if they know which of these are prime numbers. (Remember that 1 is not regarded as a prime number, so they are 2 and 3.)

Give the children some practice in finding prime factors, considering all of the numbers to 20. Ask the children what they think will happen in the case of the prime numbers themselves. (They will act as their own prime factors.)

For larger numbers the children might like to use a tree diagram to express the factorising. (This is easiest to draw on isometric paper.) To do this start with the number you wish to factorise, for example 36, and split it into its simplest factors (2 × 18). Continue to spilt each number until there are only prime factors.

9 cannot be split into 2 × anything, so look to the next prime number. If 9 had not been divisible by 3, you would have tried 5, 7, 11 and so on. The diagram below shows that the prime factors of 36 are 3 and 2:

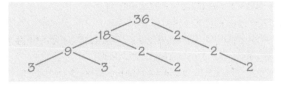

Work through another example:

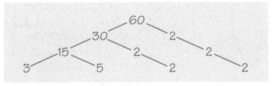

So the prime factors of 60 are 2, 3 and 5.

Ask the children to find the prime factors of 42 (2, 3 and 7) and 86 (2 and 43) to check their answers. If they complete this successfully, and seem confident, ask them to try finding the prime factors of other numbers less than 100.

DISCUSSION QUESTIONS
● *What result do you get if you split the factors differently?*

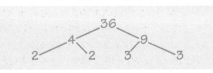

(you should still get the same prime factors)
● *How can you work systematically?*

EXTENSION
All numbers can be expressed in writing as the product of their prime factors. The factors of 24 are: 1, 2, 3, 4, 6, 8, 14 and 24. The prime factors of

24 are 2 and 3. Therefore, 24 can be expressed as the product of 2 and 3 by writing 2 × 2 × 2 × 3 or 2^3 × 3. Likewise 36 = 3 × 3 × 2 × 2 or, more economically, 3^2 x 2^2, and 60 = 2 × 2 × 3 × 5 or 2^2 × 3 × 5. Ask the children to express other numbers they have worked with in the main task as the product of their prime factors. Write up the activity using the writing frame photocopiable sheet given on page 64.

REMAINDERS

†† *Individuals or pairs, possibly working collaboratively as a class*
🕐 *30–45 minutes*

AIMS
To consider the size of remainders. To develop strategies for calculating remainders.

WHAT TO DO
Tell the children you have divided a number by 2 – what possible remainders might you have? (0 or 1)

Ask them, using different numbers as divisors, to investigate the pattern of remainders with the aim that, as a class, you might be able to write a rule about remainders something like:

'If I divide a number by 7, the biggest remainder I can get is (7 – 1) = 6. Therefore, dividing by n, the biggest possible remainder is n – 1.'

DISCUSSION QUESTIONS
● *How can we work this out systematically?*
● *What rules do you think we might get?*
● *Can we be more precise?*
(The children will need to consider how far a number is from the nearest multiple.)
● *Is there a general rule that will work whatever the divisor?*
● *Are there any things we will always need to work out before we can think about remainders?*

ASSESSMENT QUESTIONS
● *What does your rule tell you about dividing a number by 13?*
● *I find that, after dividing 345 by 15, I have got a remainder of 22. Is this reasonable? Why not?*
● *A manufacturer finds he has 13 toys left over after he has filled a series of boxes with 20 toys. How many toys might he have packaged?*
(33, 53, 73 and so on)

EXTENSION
Ask the children to write up the activity using copies of the writing frame photocopiable sheet on page 64.

DECIMAL REMAINDERS

✂ *Small groups then whole class discussion*
🕐 *20-minutes activity, followed by a 10-minute discussion*

AIMS
To consider the meaning of decimal remainders on calculator displays. To consider the link between fractions and decimals.

YOU WILL NEED
Calculators.

WHAT TO DO
Tell the children that you have just divided one number into another on your calculator and the answer has a 'point five' at the end. Ask the children what they can tell you about the two numbers you divided into each other. (One was an odd number and the other was an even number and probably 2.)

Ask the children what else they can tell you about decimal remainders. They may know that if you divide by 4 you get decimal remainders of .25 (a multiple of 4 + 1 divided by 4), .5 (a multiple of 4 + 2 divided by 4) and .75 (a multiple of 4 + 3 divided by 4).

Explain that it is sometimes useful to be able to interpret decimal remainders on a calculator and that you are going to investigate these.

Allocate each group a divisor to investigate – one group should look at dividing by 3, while others look at dividing by 4, 5, 6, 7, 8, 9, 11 and so on. Bear in mind that some of these are easier to spot than others (3, 4, 5 and 6 for example).

Remind the children that they are looking for patterns in the remainders.

DISCUSSION QUESTIONS
● *How can we investigate this systematically?*
● *How many divisions will you have to perform to make sure you have all the possible remainders?*
● *Can you make a general statement or rule which will allow us to work out what a number might have been divided by to give particular remainders?*
● *Do people from other groups feel they can use these rules?*

ASSESSMENT QUESTIONS
(Without a calculator...)
I have divided two numbers and got an answer of..., what were my two numbers?
Point out the less obvious patterns that occur in decimal remainders indicating particular divisors:

8.75 (divided by 4...(8 × 4) + 3 = 35/4)
4.3333333 (divided by 3...(4 × 3) + 1 = 13/3)
2.2857142 (divided by 7...(2 × 7) + 2 = 16/7)
3.8333333 (divided by 6...(3 × 6) + 5 = 23/6)

● *If I get an answer of 1.1818181, the number could not have been divided by 2. What else could it not have been divided by? Why?*
● *What might it have been divided by?*
● *What else can we decide about the two numbers?*
(they must be close together as the number is close to 2)

EXTENSIONS
In pairs, one child secretly enters a division into the calculator and makes a note of it. From the answer, his partner is challenged to say as much as she can about the two numbers used. She is then allowed up to four tries to work out his numbers with the calculator. She scores four points if she chooses the correct two numbers on the first go, three if they are picked on the second go, and so on. The children take turns to guess and the first child to reach ten points wins. It may be wise to restrict the size of the divisor to the numbers you have investigated.
● Write up the investigation using the writing frame photocopiable page 64.

41

MULTIPLICATION BINGO

✝✝ *Small groups, for example fours or pairs*
🕑 *30 minutes or less*

AIMS

To practise multiplying two numbers. To encourage rapid recall.

YOU WILL NEED

For each group: two 1–9 spinners, a pack of cards of the multiples to 10 × 10 (a set of 100 cards with the prime numbers over 10 removed – prime numbers are listed on page 38).

HOW TO PLAY

Deal out 16 cards to each child and ask them to arrange these in a 4 × 4 grid face up. Player 1 spins both spinners, multiplies the two numbers spun together and, if the product is in his grid, turns that card over. He passes the spinners to the next player who spins the spinners for herself. If a child has two 18s in his grid and spins a 9 and 2, he can only turn over one of the 18s and will have to wait for either another 2 and 9, or a 3 and 6, before he can turn over the second.

Any children waiting for a turn watch to make sure the calculations are correct. If a child miscalculates a product she misses her turn.

The winner is either the player with the most cards turned over after a set period of time has elapsed, or the first with a line of four cards turned over on her grid.

DISCUSSION QUESTIONS

● *What numbers do you need on the spinners to allow you to turn over this card?*
● *Do you have a better chance of covering some numbers than others?*
● *How can you predict which numbers will be easiest to make?*
● *Is there anything you can do to help yourself if you are not sure of a multiplication fact?*

(Repeated doubling for ×4 and ×8; multiply by 10 and halve for ×5; ×3 and double for ×6, and so on.)

VARIATIONS

● Deal a smaller grid (2 × 2 or 3 × 3).
● The children can work collaboratively by arranging all the cards into one big grid and then each playing as before, but working together to try to turn over as much of the grid as they can in a given time.

EXTENSION

Use multiples of all the numbers to 12 × 12. (The spinners will need to go up to 12.)

RACETRACK DIVISION

✝✝ *Two to four players*
🕑 *About 20 minutes per round*

AIM

To develop rapid recall of division facts.

YOU WILL NEED

For each group: one racetrack gameboard (given on page 60) completed with division facts likely to be known by the children from the multiplication facts (no remainders) (see example below), a set of coloured counters for each player (red for one, green for another and so on), a dice.

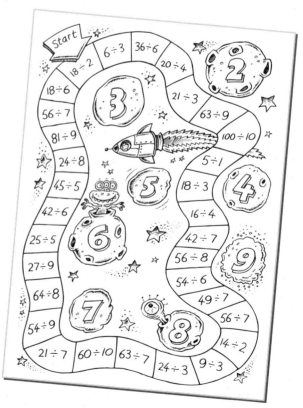

HOW TO PLAY

All players place a counter at the start. Player 1 rolls the dice and moves on that number of spaces. He solves the calculation he has landed on and places a counter on the answer circle showing the appropriate value. The dice is passed clockwise to Player 2 and play continues. The winner is the first person to place a counter on each of the answer circles. Each player can put only one counter on each answer circle, but more than one player may place his or her counters on each answer circle. If there is a disagreement the children must discuss whether an answer is correct or not and explain their reasons. If a child gets an answer wrong she misses her turn.

DISCUSSION

This game encourages rapid recall and so does not allow for much discussion. The extension games, especially the second one, encourage more discussion as they involve estimates.

VARIATION

Restrict the answer time to further encourage quick recall.

EXTENSIONS

● Change the calculations on the board to include multiples of 10 (for example, $360 \div 60$).
● Make the calculations much more difficult (for example, $856 \div 113$) and tell the children to place their counters on the 'best estimates'. Calculations such as this will need more discussion.
Questions for this extension game might include:
● *How did you make that estimate?*
● *Does everyone agree with it?*
● *Could we make a more precise estimate?*
● *How could we check if that is a good estimate?*
(By multiplying back. For example, if $378 \div 46$ is estimated to be between 7 and 8, a decision can be taken by calculating 46×7 and 46×8 to see which is nearer to 378.)

QUOTIENT & REMAINDER

†† Four players ⏱ 30 minutes

AIM

To develop the ability to find both a quotient and remainder quickly.

YOU WILL NEED

For each group: a spiral gameboard (given on photocopiable page 61, completed example above), a dice to start the game, a 2–9 spinner, one different-coloured counter each.

HOW TO PLAY

Player 1 rolls the dice and moves her counter that number of places. She spins the spinner to get a divisor, and divides the number she has landed on by the number on the spinner to find the quotient and the remainder. She is then allowed to move on an additional number of squares equal to the remainder.

For example, if you start by throwing a 3 and land on 37, you then spin the spinner and get a 4 ($37 \div 4 = 8$ r1). So you move one more square. You will need to decide how to finish the game – must the children land exactly on 'Finish' or can they go past it?
Note: the children could note the facts that give them the most trouble and learn these as homework.

DISCUSSION QUESTIONS

● *What will divide exactly into that number and leave no remainders?*
● *What divisor will give you the biggest remainder? How do you know?*

VARIATION

Include 10, 11 and 12 as divisors on the spinner or make a simpler spinner by restricting the numbers to 2, 5, and 10.

EXTENSION

Make a baseboard with three-digit numbers and include 49, 50 and 51, or 24, 25 and 26 on the spinner.

STRATEGIES

CHILDREN SHOULD BE WORKING WITH NUMBERS OF THE ORDER:

● as given on pages 10 for counting and ordering, 18 for addition and subtraction and 28 for multiplication and division.

AS A MINIMUM, BY THE END OF YEAR 6/PRIMARY 7 MOST CHILDREN SHOULD BE ABLE TO:

● count forwards and backwards in steps of any size;
● read and order and know the place value of the digit in any number, including decimals and negative numbers;
● read and order a set of mixed numbers (such as 174, 17.4, 7.14, 1.74, 0.174, 74.1, 1.004, 74.01);
● read and order mixed and vulgar fractions (including tenths and hundredths), converting between the two if necessary.

For addition and subtraction:
● use known addition and subtraction facts to 20;
● add a series of one-digit numbers;
● approximate answers to calculations by rounding;
● use simple known fractions such as $\frac{1}{2}, \frac{1}{3}, \frac{1}{4}, \frac{1}{5}, \frac{1}{6}, \frac{1}{8}, \frac{1}{10}$;
● use known decimals to at least one and then two decimal places in the context of measures and money;
● use the 24 hour clock and timetables.

For multiplication and division:
● recall multiplication and division facts to 10 x 10;
● recall doubles of numbers to 50, then 100, and their corresponding halves.

Further detail is given on pages 10 for counting and ordering, 18 for addition and subtraction and 28 for multiplication and division.

The children will need to use strategies they have developed elsewhere to solve these calculations involving several steps using different operations. However, at the heart of solving mixed operation and multistep problems are decisions about the maths to use and the order in which to approach the problems.

USEFUL STRATEGIES FOR MAKING DECISIONS ABOUT THE MATHS NEEDED

asking the children to rephrase the question or problem;

encouraging the children to consider the information they have and make a list of it all – to separate the information from the problem;

encouraging the children to write open number sentences that reflect the narrative sense of the problems.

OPEN NUMBER SENTENCES

Consider this rather simple problem:

Simon collects stamps. He has 73 stamps and his album holds 120. How many more stamps must Simon collect to fill the stamp album?

Many adults will represent this as 120 – 73 = ?, transforming the problem directly into the number sentence needed to answer it. This does not reflect, however, the narrative sense of the problem. This narrative sense might be better reflected in an open number sentence (one where the unknown quantity is not at the end) such as: 73 + ? = 120. This second option is more useful to pupils learning to tackle this type of problem. It is more likely to fit with their understanding of the problem.

Transforming problems into number sentences that indicate an answer 'at the end' is a common adult strategy – but this process of transformation is difficult and often far from clear to children.

Children's access to problems and open number sentences (where the unknown is not at the end) is often restricted because adults feel that these are more difficult. Research* indicates that where children are taught to read and use all number sentence types then they are more successful at solving problems. The range of problems that need consideration might be represented by the following expressions, as well as multistep number operations using brackets:

$? + b = c$	$a + ? = c$	$a + ? = c$
$? - b = c$	$a - ? = c$	$a - b = ?$
$? \times b = c$	$a \times ? = c$	$a \times b = ?$
$? \div b = c$	$a \div ? = c$	$a \div b = ?$

OTHER THINGS TO TRY

Estimating an answer first is especially important in tackling multistep problems as there are more opportunities to make an error in calculation or to tackle steps to the solution in the wrong order (or to omit a step).

Writing stories or problems to illustrate number sentences as well as encouraging children to write number sentences to reflect problems will help them to develop confidence with the full range of possibilities listed previously.

Multistep problems often confuse children. They get very used to being asked questions which require only one piece of mathematics to answer them. A valuable activity is to discuss with the children questions such as:

> If we wanted to take the class to France for a day trip what would we need to find out? What calculations would we need to do?

> If the government decided to buy a book for all Year 6 children going up to secondary school this year how could we work out how much this would cost?

> I want to take my parents and my sister to London to visit the zoo. How much money will I need?

> The Department of Transport have to repaint the white lines along the whole length of the A1(M) - how could they work out how much white paint they will need to order?

This will give them opportunities to consider and think through problems. These processes can then be reflected upon and the children may be able to develop some reminders for themselves.

* Carpenter, TJ, Moser, JM and Bebout, H (1988) 'Representation of addition and subtraction word problems' in *Journal for Research in Mathematics Education*, 19/4/345–57.

MULTISTEP AND MIXED OPERATIONS

I'M THINKING OF A NUMBER

†† *Whole class* 🕐 *5-10 minutes*

AIMS

To encourage children to formulate questions. To encourage use of knowledge of the properties of number.

WHAT TO DO

Tell the children you are thinking of a number. They can ask you questions to find out what the number is, but you will only answer 'Yes' or 'No', so they will have to think carefully about how they phrase their questions.

Children who have not played this sort of game before generally have very few strategies for planning questions and will tend to start by asking 'Is it 25?' or 'Is it greater than 10?' They should be encouraged to see that these are not very useful questions. One way to help them develop strategies is to set limits when you start playing the game. So, for example, you might say: 'I am thinking of a number between 0 and 100'. If you encourage the children to think about how many numbers your number could be (in this case 100), and how many possible numbers the question they are planning to ask rules in (or out), then they will quickly grasp that they will learn more from a question such as 'Is it an odd number?' than 'Is it greater than 10?'

Once children become more expert at asking the questions, you can start limiting the numbers of particular question types they are allowed. For example, you might say that they can only ask 'Is it greater than...?' once.

The purpose of this game is to encourage the use of a range of vocabulary associated with describing numbers. This might include: greater than, smaller than, multiple of, factor of, divisible by, prime, positive, negative, integer (whole number), fraction, vulgar fraction, proper fraction, mixed fraction and decimal fraction.

DISCUSSION QUESTIONS

● *Is that a useful question?*
● *What can you tell me about my number at this stage?*
● *What would be a useful thing to find out next? Can you think of a question that would allow you to find that out?*
● *How did you decide to ask that question?*
● *What kinds of questions are most useful?*
● *How many questions has it taken to find my number?*

ASSESSMENT QUESTIONS

● *Could you have found my number with fewer questions?*
● *Which questions were not particularly helpful?*
● *Which questions would have been more useful?*

EXTENSIONS

● Try using decimal numbers, fractions of various sorts and very large numbers. These are more difficult to work out than whole numbers between 1 and 100.
● Limit the number of questions a child can ask.
● Write a list of useful questions for eliminating particular types of number.

MISSING OPERATION

†† *Whole class* 🕐 *5-10 minutes*

AIM

To encourage children to think of the effects of operations.

WHAT TO DO

Think of a number sentence with at least three stages such as 13 – 9 × 7 = 28.

Write it up with one of the operands missing, perhaps: 13 __ 9 × 7 = 28. Tell the children that it is to be read from left to right or, if you prefer, use brackets to signal the order (13__9) × 7 = 28. This makes things much easier, but may provide an opportunity to explain how brackets indicate the order of calculation if the children have not been introduced to this concept before.

Ask what the missing operation is then write up another number sentence for them to try.

DISCUSSION QUESTIONS

● *How did you solve this?*
● *Who used trial and improvement?*
● *Did you estimate first?*
● *What did you use to help you estimate?*
● *Did anyone use a different method to help them find the answer?*

- *Can you explain your method?*
- *Which is more efficient? Why?*
- *Did anyone use what they know about inverse operations to work backwards?*

ASSESSMENT QUESTION

Can you use that method to solve this question? (keep the format of the number sentence the same, for instance: $9 - 3 \times 8 = 48$)

EXTENSIONS

- Vary the operations you use and the order in which you use them.
- Set up a worksheet at a suitable level (see below) and ask the children to complete it. They should write an explanation of how they found the solution beside each question.

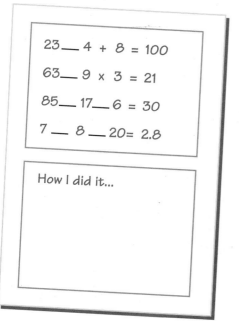

$$23 \_\_ 4 + 8 = 100$$
$$63 \_\_ 9 \times 3 = 21$$
$$85 \_\_ 17 \_\_ 6 = 30$$
$$7 \_\_ 8 \_\_ 20 = 2.8$$

How I did it...

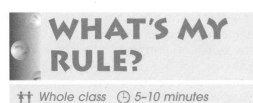

WHAT'S MY RULE?

†† *Whole class* ⏱ *5–10 minutes*

AIMS

To encourage children to ask questions and think about the properties of numbers. To encourage the precise use of mathematical language.

WHAT TO DO

Decide on a rule such as 'All multiples of 3', 'Factors of 48', 'All numbers less than 2' and so on.

Draw up a chart with two columns, large enough for everyone to see. Label the columns 'Numbers that obey my rule' and 'Numbers that do not obey my rule'.

Tell the children that you are thinking of a rule and that they must try to work out what it is.

They can do this by giving you numbers – you will tell them whether each number obeys your rule. You will not be able to give them any more help than that. Once they think they have guessed your rule they can ask to share it.

It is important to encourage precision in the use of language. One way to do this, once children have got the hang of the game, is to make up rules such as 'Even numbers less than 50'.

It is important to note that, while it is generally fairly easy to find numbers that will obey a rule, it is more useful to try testing the rules' limits by seeking numbers that will not obey it. An example of this might be having a rule such as 'All numbers with a 5 in the '1s' column'. If children stick to testing only whole numbers they will probably guess at numbers like 25.3. 'Numbers divisible by 5' will also obey this rule.

DISCUSSION QUESTIONS

- *What kinds of numbers have you tried?*
- *What other kinds of numbers are there?* (fractional, decimal, over 100, negative and so on)
- *What do you think my rule is?*
- *What do other people think of that definition?*
- *Can you help him to see why that is not a good question?*

ASSESSMENT QUESTIONS

- *Is that definition precise enough?*
- *Are there any other numbers that might obey that rule that you haven't tried yet?*

EXTENSIONS

- Limit the number of attempts allowed to guess the rule.
- If a child is not participating make that person the 'rule offerer', so that any time a child wants to suggest a rule they have to do it through the 'rule offerer'.

WHAT AM I DOING?

†† *Whole class* ⏱ *5–10 minutes*

AIM

To encourage the children to think about the effects of different operations on different kinds of numbers.

WHAT TO DO

Tell the children that you are thinking of an operation, and that if they give you a number you will tell them what has happened to the number after you have applied your operation. Write both

MULTISTEP AND MIXED OPERATIONS

the original and final number up so that all the children can see them both. For example, you might choose to multiply by 7. Draw up two columns, one headed 'In' and the other 'Out'. If a child suggests 5 you would write 5 in the 'In' column and '35' in the 'Out' column.

x 7	
In	Out
5	35

When they think they have worked out what your operation is, the children may offer to tell you their answer. If you judge that most of the class have still not worked it out then ask the child with the answer to wait until a few more people have 'got it'. Beware of making statements such as 'Multiplying makes bigger'. This is only true in the context of whole numbers and over-generalisation can lead to problems with rules such as 'Multiply by 0.5'.

Note: If you have access to an overhead projector calculator, put the operation in as a constant function and then allow children to come and enter numbers themselves. They will enjoy this. If you are using more complex operations, you might want access to a calculator yourself!

DISCUSSION QUESTIONS
When a large proportion of the class have 'got it', rather than just asking them to tell you the rule, suggest an 'In' number and ask them to tell you the number that will come out.
● *What is the operation?*
● *How do you know?*
● *Is there anything else it could be?*

ASSESSMENT QUESTION
● *Is there a question you could ask to make absolutely sure?*
(for multiplication, ×1 will leave the number unchanged, dividing by 1 will give you your original number, and adding and subtracting 0 leaves a number unchanged)

EXTENSIONS
● The kinds of operation you choose will depend upon the class. You may wish to start with straightforward operations and move on to two-step operations such as 'Double and add 1', 'Multiply by three-quarters'.
● Alternatively, rather than doing something to the number suggested, use it to do something to another number; for example, 'Take from 100' so that 20 'In' becomes 80 'Out'.

THERE AND BACK AGAIN

†† *Whole class*   ⏲ *10–15 minutes*

AIM
To consider inverse operations.

WHAT TO DO
Draw up a copy of a function machine like the one below:

'Put in' different numbers and ask the children to tell you what will 'come out' at each stage. For example, putting in 6 will give:

Change the functions and repeat the process.

DISCUSSION QUESTIONS
● *If I start a new function machine and tell you that the number at the half-way point is 18, can you tell me what I will end up with? Is that difficult to work out?*
● *What number did I start with?*
● *How could we work that out?*
● *How could we check?*

ASSESSMENT QUESTION
Ask the children to work from the 'out' numbers:
● *If I end up with 45, what number did I put in?*

EXTENSIONS
● Tell the children each to make up a function machine, then give their friends some numbers to put in to see what will come out. They could also try giving them some 'exit numbers' to see if they can work out the original numbers.
● Encourage the children to write up their findings on the writing frame photocopiable sheet given on page 64.

PRICE CHANGE

†† *Whole class* ⏱ *5–10 minutes*

AIM

To develop strategies for calculating percentage increases and decreases.

WHAT TO DO

This activity is part of the game 'Shop 'til you drop' given on page 56. Prepare a list of items on the board or overhead projector with prices such as:

Dress	£50.00
Coat	£75.00
Hat	£35.00
Video recorder	£100.00
Stereo	£150.00
Answerphone	£120.00
Socks	£4.00
Gloves	£10.00
Scarf	£20.00

Prepare a set of cards (as for the game) with percentage increases and decreases marked: 10%, 15%, 20%, 25%, 50% and so on.

Pick an item (such as the video recorder) and shuffle the price change cards. Ask a child to pick a card and read it aloud. Then ask everyone to calculate the new price.

DISCUSSION QUESTIONS

● *What is the new price?*
● *How did you calculate that?*
● *Did anyone do it differently?*

ASSESSMENT QUESTION

What would happen to the price of the scarf under the same price change?

EXTENSION

Play the game 'Shop 'til you drop' (page 56).

INTERPRETING PIE CHARTS

†† *Whole class* ⏱ *10–15 minutes*

AIMS

To develop an awareness of some of the uses and misuses of pie charts as a means of representing data – especially when comparing pie charts.

WHAT TO DO

Draw up the two pie charts below so that all the children can see them.

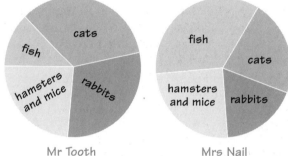

Mr Tooth   Mrs Nail

Explain that the charts show how much of two pet shop owners' profit is made from selling different types of animal. Tell them that Mr Tooth made £350 selling cats, then ask them to estimate how much he makes selling fish. (£70)

Can they tell about how much money each shopkeeper makes from selling each kind of animal? Who sells more of each type?

Tell them that in one week last July Mr Tooth made a total of £1 000 and Mrs Nail made £800. Then ask them to estimate how much of that each shopkeeper made from selling hamsters and mice. (about $\frac{1}{4}$, so £250 and £200 respectively)
Note: The children should understand that, when comparing percentages, they need to know the sample size. For example, 25% of 600 is much less than 25% of 6000, although they will look the same on a pie chart.

DISCUSSION QUESTIONS

● *Why might you have to be careful interpreting pie charts?*
● *With what other kinds of statistics might you need to be careful when you start making comparisons?*
(percentages and averages, amongst others)

EXTENSIONS

● Find two real pie charts in a newspaper. Discuss what they tell you; what information is missing (if any) and how they might be misinterpreted.
● The class could compare pie charts using the writing frame photocopiable sheet on page 64.

MULTISTEP AND MIXED OPERATIONS

MULTISTEP AND MIXED OPERATIONS

RAIL TRAVEL

†† *Individual or small group*
🕑 *20–30 minutes*

AIMS

To give practice at getting information from a table and interpreting the data. To offer practice in calculating time.

WHAT TO DO

Give the child or group a copy of the table opposite. Explain that the prices have been converted into decimal money so that they can be compared with modern fares.

Ask some or all of the following questions:
● How many more times more expensive was it to travel first class to Edinburgh in 1990 than it was in 1900? (approximately 25 times)
● About what fraction of the first class fare is the third class fare? Has there always been about the same differential? (about $\frac{2}{3}$, though in 1960 it was slightly closer to $\frac{4}{5}$)
● What would the cost of the journey to Edinburgh have been for a group of four adults travelling first class in 1940?
● How much could they have saved by going third class?
● How much longer did it take to make the journey in 1900 than in 1990?
● Why has the journey become so much faster? (electrification of the track, non-stop services, more streamlined trains and so on)
● When did the biggest reduction in journey time occur? (between 1960 and 1970)
● Why might journey times have increased in 1920 and 1940? (perhaps because of the two world wars)

Think up some more questions of your own to ask or challenge the children to make up some more to ask their friends.

DISCUSSION QUESTIONS

● *How did you calculate the answers?*
● *How could we make a decision about when the journey represented the best value for money?*

● *What other information should we collect?* (average wages, cost of everyday items, or the cost of travelling by another means of transport)
● *How could we calculate the price per hour travelling?* (or the cost per mile or kilometre?)

EXTENSIONS

● Draw line graphs to overlay the journey time, and the cost of first and second class tickets over time. Ask the children what they notice.
● What general statements can they make?
● When did things change most rapidly?
● How can the children tell? (from where the graph is steepest)

The cost of a rail ticket from London to Edinburgh, 1900–1990				
Year	Journey time		Fare (Single)*	
	hr	min	First	Third
1900	8	30	2.88	1.63
1910	8	30	2.88	1.63
1920	9	00	N/A	N/A
1930	8	15	4.09(est)	2.46(est)
1940	8	56	4.30(est)	2.58(est)
1950	7	54	6.72	4.30
1960	7	02	5.33	3.50
1970	5	48	8.70	5.70
1980	4	37	37.00	25.60
1990	4	32	76.00	54.00

* Third Class became Second Class in 1956. This is now called Standard Class.

THEATRE ATTENDANCE

†† *Individuals, pairs or small groups*
🕑 *About 45 minutes*

AIM

To provide practice at interpreting line graphs and manipulating large numbers.

WHAT TO DO

Provide each pair or small group with a copy of the graph and explain that it shows how many people made a visit to a theatre each month during 1996. Ask them some questions like these:
● Which month had the largest/smallest attendance? (December/August)

- What is the difference between the greatest/smallest attendance? (24 000)
- What is the average attendance over the winter months? (30 000)
- What is the difference between the average summer and winter attendance? (20 000)

DISCUSSION QUESTIONS

- *What does this graph tell you?*
- *What trends do you notice?*
- *What reasons can you think of for these trends?*
- *What strategies can you use to help you when you are calculating with very large numbers?*

EXTENSIONS

- The attendance for this year is 25% up on the attendance during the year the graph was made. What are this year's attendance figures?
- If one-fifth of the people attending the theatre are children, how much does the theatre take in an average month (adult tickets cost £12 and child tickets cost £6)?
- What is the difference between the average ticket sales and the ticket sales in the best month? What is the difference between the average, and the worst month?

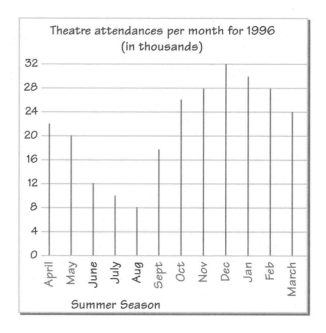

SWIMMERS

†† Individuals/pairs/small groups
🕐 15 minutes

AIM

To practise calculating with time, including decimal expressions with tenths and hundredths.

WHAT TO DO

Explain that times for sporting events are recorded in **minutes**, **seconds** and **tenths and hundredths of seconds**. So a time of **3: 4.25** is 'three minutes: four point 25 seconds', and the point 25 is equal to a quarter of a second.

Make sure everyone can see a copy of the table below.

100m freestyle		4 × 200m medley	
Alan	49.43	Swimmer 1	3: 14.40
Terry	48.42	Swimmer 2	3: 23.27
Paul	50.67	Swimmer 3	3: 25.03
John	51.48	Swimmer 4	3: 17.30

Now ask some of the following questions:
- Who won the 100m freestyle? (Make sure, in advance, that everyone realises the winner is the swimmer who records the smallest time.)
- What time separated Alan and Terry?
- What time separated the winner from fourth?
- What was the average time?
- Who swam fastest in the 4 × 200m medley?
- How long did the race last?
- What was the average speed in this race?

DISCUSSION QUESTIONS

- *How can you calculate the averages mentally?*
- *How did you calculate the total time for the 4 × 200m medley?*
- *Did you find any short cuts to help you?* (add the 4 × 3 minutes at the end, look for numbers that combine to give subtotals that are easier to manage, and so on)

Tell the children that the fastest fish in the world is the sailfish. It can reach speeds of 100 km/hr.
- *How long would it take a sailfish to swim 100m? 800m?**
- *What would be the time difference between Terry and the sailfish over 100m; and the human swimming team and the sailfish over 800m?*
*Note: 100km/hr = 100 000m per 3600secs, dividing by 1000 gives us a speed of 100m in 3.6secs.

EXTENSIONS

- When else do we need to measure really accurately?
- What instruments do we use to help us get very accurate measurements?

Theatre attendances per month for 1996 (in thousands)

A bar chart with y-axis labelled 0 to 32 in intervals of 4, and x-axis months: April, May, June, July, Aug, Sept, Oct, Nov, Dec, Jan, Feb, March. Labelled "Summer Season".

MULTISTEP AND MIXED OPERATIONS

FORESTATION

†† *Individuals or small groups*
⏱ *20–30 minutes*

AIM
To give practice at comparing percentages and reading and interpreting graphical data.

WHAT TO DO
Give each child or group a suitably-sized copy of the graph below and then ask some or all of the following questions:
● Which country has the greatest forest coverage? (Brazil)
● Which has the least? (UK)
● What is the average forest cover? (36.43%)
● How much greater than the average is the most forested country? (30.67%)
● How much less forested than the average is the least forested country? (27.03%)
● Which country is closest to the average? (Vietnam)
● What percentage of land is not forested in each country?

DISCUSSION QUESTIONS
● *These figures are about 10 years old. Would you expect today's statistics to be different? How?*
● *How did you calculate your answers?*
● *How could we find out the actual coverage for each country? What additional information would we need?*
● *The area of the UK is approximately 244 000km². What is the approximate area of forest in the UK? How do you know?*

EXTENSIONS
● Estimate the density of trees in a forest. How many trees might there be in forests in the UK?
● Encourage the children to use atlases to find out the land areas for the other countries in the graph and work out actual areas of forestation.

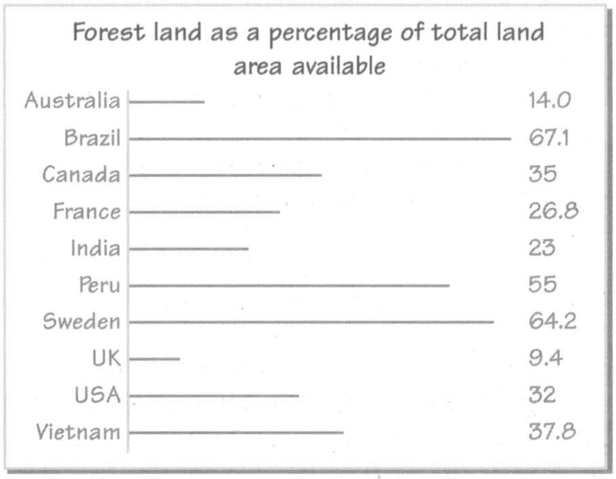

Forest land as a percentage of total land area available	
Australia	14.0
Brazil	67.1
Canada	35
France	26.8
India	23
Peru	55
Sweden	64.2
UK	9.4
USA	32
Vietnam	37.8

Name	Distance	Points
Amy	1.90m	6
Barry	1.96m	6
David	1.43m	4
Gurdeep	2.10m	7
Kate	1.27m	3
Mike	1.56m	4
Meg	1.98m	6
Peter	1.50m	4
Siu Mei	2.09m	7
Tanya	2.12m	7

AVERAGE SCORES

†† *Whole class* ⏱ *10–15 minutes*

AIM
To give practice in addition and division in the context of finding averages.

WHAT TO DO
Draw up the chart above so that everyone can see it. Explain that it contains the results of a long jump competition.
   Then ask questions such as:
● Who won? Who came last?
● What was the difference in the distance jumped between: David and Peter? Barry and Siu Mei? Siu Mei and Gurdeep?
● The girls were competing as a team against the boys. Which team got more points? (girls)
● What was the average point score for the girls? (6) And the boys? (5)
● Can you put the competitors in order?
● Max arrived after the competition. He jumped a distance exactly half-way between Siu Mei's and Barry's. How far was this? How would you write that? (2.025m)

DISCUSSION QUESTIONS
● *How have you worked that out?*
● *What do we mean by an average?*
● *What other mathematical word do we use for average?*
(mean)
● *What is the range of the scores (the difference between the greatest and the smallest)?*

EXTENSIONS
Answer these questions orally or in writing:
● Find the combined total jumped by the girls and the boys (or all the children).
● Find the average distance jumped.

DEVELOPING MENTAL MATHS

HOW MANY WAYS?

†† *Large group introduction and conclusion, then individuals*
🕐 *About 45 minutes*

AIM
To work flexibly to generate number sentences with the full range of number operations.

WHAT TO DO
Begin with a large group introduction. Ask the children if they can think of any number sentences they might write which equal 20. Initially, they may come up with answers such as 19 + 1, 20 × 1, 10 × 2, or 4 × 5. Accept these, but then ask if they can make more complex number sentences. Specify that the sentences must contain at least two operations. You may want to further specify that they should not use simple inverse operations – so 19 + 3 – 2 would be unacceptable, while 4 × 4 + 4 would be fine.

Tell the children to find as many number sentences as they can that obey the above criteria. (Allow a time limit of perhaps 5 minutes.)

Discuss the strategies they are using. (They may find it helpful to break the 20 into parts, perhaps 16 + 4, and then find ways of making each part, so 16 = 4 × 4, 2 × 8, 10 + 6 and so on.)

If the children have strategies for working systematically, impose further conditions (see 'Extensions' below). Allow them to continue to work for 5 or 10 more minutes and then discuss their strategies again.

DISCUSSION QUESTIONS
● *How can you work systematically?*
● *Did you use any of your previous sentences to write this one?*
● *What new sentences could you generate from this one?*
● *Which sentence types were most difficult to generate?*
● *Why do you think that is?*
● *Which numbers and operations are most useful?*
● *Are there any numbers you can see you haven't used?*
(check the use of odd numbers)
● *Which is the longest number sentence anyone has written?*

ASSESSMENT QUESTION
Offer the children more open challenges such as:
● *Can you make a number sentence which uses three operations and totals 40?*

EXTENSIONS
● Impose conditions: the use of three operations; at least one proper fraction or one decimal.
● Ask the children to write up the investigation on the writing frame photocopiable on page 64.

IN OR OUT OF BRACKETS?

†† *Individual and larger group*
🕐 *About 45 minutes*

AIM
To introduce the conventions for using brackets.

YOU WILL NEED
Calculators (both scientific and simple).

WHAT TO DO
Write up a number sentence such as: '4 + 3 × 5 ='. (A scientific calculator will give an answer of 19 for this, while a simple calculator will give an answer of 35.) Ask the children to calculate the answer mentally first, then on the two calculators. Discuss the two answers and introduce brackets. Explain that the simple calculator has worked out (4 + 3) × 5 = 7 × 5 = 35, while the scientific calculator has done 4 + (3 × 5) = 4 + 15 = 19.

Explain that there is a convention that in expressions without brackets (or once brackets have been calculated) division and multiplication should be carried out before addition and subtraction: BODMAS (**B**rackets **O**ver **D**ivision, **M**ultiplication, **A**ddition and **S**ubtraction). Ask which answer fits the BODMAS convention (19).

Work, as a group, through two or three more examples, exploring the use of brackets. Ask the children, using the digits 2, 5, 3, 8, in that order, with the four operations and brackets and the BODMAS convention, how many numbers they can generate? (2 + 5) – 3 × 8, 2 + (5 – 3) × 8...

DISCUSSION QUESTIONS
● *How can you work systematically?*
● *Did anyone else get (32)?*
● *Did you use the same number sentence to generate that number?*
● *Is it possible to find another number sentence that will give (32) as an answer?*

ASSESSMENT QUESTIONS
Give the children incomplete expressions, for example 452342 = 44.
● *Keeping the numerals in the same order and placing necessary operation signs and brackets, can you make the number sentence correct?*
((45 – 23) × 4 ÷ 2 = 44)

DEVELOPING MENTAL MATHS

MULTISTEP AND MIXED OPERATIONS

FIVES ON A NUMBER LINE

†† *Pairs, threes or fours* ⏱ *30 minutes*

AIMS

To develop flexible methods for generating particular numbers using all four operations. To reinforce which numbers are multiples of 5.

YOU WILL NEED

For each group: three or four sets of 1–10 cards shuffled together, a 100 number line (or number square), some small counters that will cover a number on the line or square without obscuring others.

HOW TO PLAY

Place a counter on any number that is a multiple of 5 along the whole length of the number line. Deal three cards to the first player. She uses the cards and any of the four operations to try to make a multiple of 5 and then describe her method to the other players. All three cards must be used and each card can be used only once.

If they agree with the calculation, Player 1 takes the counter from that number (for example, $(7 \times 4) + 2 = 30$). Player 2 then has three cards dealt to him and play continues as above. The winner is the child with most counters at the end of the game. A system of arbitration may need to be agreed in case of disputes.

DISCUSSION QUESTIONS

● *Which numbers did you find hardest/easiest to make?*
● *Does everyone find the same numbers difficult? Why do you think that might be?*

VARIATIONS

● Let the children play collaboratively – allow pairs to work together against other pairs.
● If the children agree on which numbers are most difficult to make, you could put two counters on these numbers so there is an extra incentive to try to work them out!

EXTENSIONS

● Use a –50 to +50 number line and make some of the cards negative.
● Use 0–200 number lines and deal four cards to each player.
● Play this game with the counters placed on other multiples (perhaps multiples of 10 or 6).

NUMBER SENTENCES

†† *Pairs or fours* ⏱ *20–30 minutes*

AIM

To develop flexible use of all four operations.

YOU WILL NEED

For each pair or group: a pack of ten target numbers shuffled together, face down ('randomly' chosen – you could choose ten decade numbers, or keep the numbers below 100, or have answers with simple decimals such as 6.5, and so on), a pack of 1–50 number cards, several cards with operation signs.

HOW TO PLAY

Lay out the 1–50 cards and the operation sign cards face up on the table. Player 1 turns over a target number and takes the number cards and operations required to make that number (for example, for a target number of 20 the child could take $19 + 1$, 4×5 and so on) and reads his number sentence to the other players. If they agree that the number sentence makes the target number then Player 1 keeps the number cards and the target number and replaces the operation cards. Play passes to Player 2 who takes a new target number, and so on.

If a target number cannot be reached it is put to one side and the player does not keep any cards for that turn. The winner is the player with the most target cards at the end of play.

Since the number cards are not replaced, each turn gets progressively more difficult. If a child cannot make her target number because the remaining number cards do not allow the target to be reached, play passes to the next player and the target card is put to one side. If all players, in turn, cannot make their target numbers then all cards should be returned to the centre, signalling the end of the game or the start of another round. A different player should start each round.

DISCUSSION QUESTIONS

● *What number sentence hit that target?*
● *How else could you have reached that target?*
● *Which number cards are most/least useful?*

VARIATIONS

● The game may be played co-operatively with the aim of making number sentences for as many of the target numbers as possible.
● Change the target numbers, perhaps including halves or negative numbers in the target numbers.

EXTENSION

Encourage the children also to make up a number story to accompany each number sentence. For example, for 5 × 6 + 9 = 39 the child might say 'The shopkeeper sold five comics every day for six days, then the next day he sold nine. So in that week he sold 39 comics.'

TARGET THE NUMBER

†† *Two to six players* 🕒 *As long as you like*

AIM

To develop a variety of methods for reaching a target number with all four operations.

YOU WILL NEED

For each group: two sets of 2–10 cards shuffled together, a set of target numbers (possibly a set of 0–100 cards from which to pick).

HOW TO PLAY

Player 1 deals out four cards face up in the centre of the table and chooses a target number (for example, 32) from the pack available. All players then use the four numbers and any operations to reach the target number. Each group member works on making all target numbers. So, if the four cards dealt were 1, 2, 7 and 8, then 32 could be made by 2 × (7 + 1 + 8). Each number can be used only once.

DISCUSSION QUESTIONS

● *Who got to the target number? What methods have you all used?*
● *Which is the most efficient method?*

● *How did you go about working that out?*
● *Who used a different strategy to get started?*

VARIATIONS

● Keep the same target number but deal four new number cards for each round.
● Keep the same four number cards and choose a new target number for each round.

EXTENSIONS

● Add in some larger numbers to the 2–10 cards, such as 12, 25, 50 or 100.
● Generate targets <1000 by picking three single-digit cards and placing them together.

MY TURN NEXT

†† *Pairs, threes or fours* 🕒 *About 30 minutes*

AIM

To develop flexible approaches to the four number operations when making numbers to 100.

YOU WILL NEED

For each group: three sets of 1–10 cards, a 1–100 square, a set of different-coloured counters for each player.

HOW TO PLAY

Shuffle all the cards and deal out four to each player. Place the rest of the pack face down on the table.

ROUND 1

Player 1 starts, looks at her four cards (say 2, 4, 5 and 6) and nominates the number she will make (for example 36).
Player 2 (and others, if appropriate) do the same. Player 1 says how she got her total ((5 × 6) + 2 + 4). If all other players agree, then she places her counter on that number on the square. If she has made an error she misses her turn. This procedure is repeated for all the players. All four cards must be used each time, but each card can be used only once in each turn.

ROUND 2

Four new cards each are dealt, but this time Player 2 starts and play continues as before. Continue until one child has put his counters on four numbers in a row on the square. These can be in any direction.

Note: Children often start by trying to make numbers near the top of the 100 square perceiving these to be easiest, in fact it is best to start near the centre of the board and not too close to a prime number.

MULTISTEP AND MIXED OPERATIONS

DISCUSSION QUESTIONS

● *Where is the best place to have your start number? Why?*
● *What other numbers could you have made with those four cards?*
● *What numbers could you make next? Which of those will be easiest/hardest to make?*
● *What number cards do you need to make your next number?*

It is often worth helping children with 'tricks' if they do not try these for themselves – such as to multiply by 5, multiply by 10 and halve, or to multiply by 4 or 8 use repeated doubling.

VARIATIONS

● Let the children play co-operatively to see how many numbers they can cover.
● The game could be made easier by using three cards and making lines of three.

EXTENSIONS

● To make this game more difficult, use six cards and make lines of six.
● Replace the three sets of 1–10 cards with a combination of one- and two-digit numbers or use decimal and fraction cards. (Note: you will need to change the number square used for these.)

SHOP 'TIL YOU DROP

†† *Two to four players*   ⏲ *About 30 minutes*

AIM

To give practice and develop strategies for calculating percentage price increases and decreases.

YOU WILL NEED

For each group: the gameboard on page 63 (preferably enlarged to A3), a 1–6 dice and a 1–10 spinner, a copy of the store's stock list (given on page 62), a set of price increase cards and a set of discount cards marked with appropriate percentages and shuffled together.

HOW TO PLAY

The price increase and discount cards might start as 10%, 25%, 50%, and move on to include percentages that can be built from these basic starters (5%, 15%, 20%, 75%) and then percentages that are multiples of 10% such as 30%, 40%, 60% and so on. Later you might want to introduce percentages that require two different types of calculation (such as 35%, 45% and so on), or longer additive solutions, such as VAT at 17.5% which can be calculated as 10% + 5% + 2.5%,

each part of which can be calculated by halving the one before.

The aim of the game is to visit all the shop's departments at least once and return to the exit. The first player to get right around the store and back out through the exit wins.

Player 1 throws the 1–6 dice and moves a number of squares equal to the number he has thrown. Moves can be made in a straight line only (no diagonal moves). Once he is in a department he must spin the 1–10 spinner to choose an item from the stock list for that department and then pick a price change card. He must calculate the increase or decrease and tell the other players what he needs to pay. If they agree with his new price he can move on when his next turn comes, waiting in the meantime while the other players take their turns. If he makes a mistake in calculating the new price incorrectly, he must try to do it again on his next turn *without* moving on.

Players must make a price change calculation every time it is their turn (even if they remain in the same department for more than one go). Once a price change card has been used it is replaced at the bottom of the pack.

Items from the stock list can be used more than once.

DISCUSSION QUESTIONS

● *What calculations are you going to need to carry out?*
● *What methods will you use?*
● *Has she calculated that correctly?*
● *Does that new price seem about right? Is it right?*
● *Which strategies are useful?*
● *Is it easier to calculate increases in price or decreases? Why is that?*
● *Would you need to round the new price up or down to make it sensible?*

VARIATIONS

● To make the game simpler use only increase cards or only decrease cards.
● Make up a new stock list.

EXTENSION

Vary the percentage changes on the 'price change' cards.

PUBLIC LIBRARIES ACTUALS 1995-96

	County or District	Total Bookstock	Total Children's Books	% of Children's Books of Total Bookstock
1	Hampshire	3 260 252	1 655 846	51
2	Lancashire	3 122 751	1 852 445	59
3	Essex	3 041 276	1 675 650	55
4	Kent	2 843 821	2 515 881	88
5	Devon	2 397 526	2 001 339	83
6	Hertfordshire	2 313 314	1 367 881	59
7	Glasgow	2 247 330	602 294	27
8	Manchester	1 991 470	910 099	46
9	Nottinghamshire	1 979 066	1 151 437	58
10	Surrey	1 951 152	1 516 217	78
11	Staffordshire	1 803 639	1 357 709	75
12	Cheshire	1 697 131	975 817	57
13	Avon	1 688 106	782 109	46
14	Leicestershire	1 610 384	1 069 019	66
15	Derbyshire	1 590 150	794 419	50
16	Belfast	1 450 341	320 612	22
17	Leeds	1 422 333	749 242	53
18	Liverpool	1 374 935	645 592	47
19	Lincolnshire	1 359 635	631 303	46
20	Cambridgeshire	1 348 401	815 885	61
21	East Sussex	1 312 771	762 478	58
22	Norfolk	1 297 634	704 290	54
23	Buckinghamshire	1 273 452	648 890	51
24	North Yorkshire	1 268 199	620 692	49
25	Edinburgh	1 231 308	627 499	51
26	West Sussex	1 189 931	665 293	56
27	Durham	1 159 399	506 913	44
28	Dorset	1 147 081	841 959	73
29	Wiltshire	1 146 264	622 473	54
30	Northamptonshire	1 107 506	701 070	63
31	Somerset	1 098 236	641 807	58
32	Berkshire	1 083 165	732 832	68
33	North Eastern	1 044 546	586 418	56
34	Oxfordshire	1 035 629	547 260	53
35	Cornwall	1 027 617	846 910	82
36	Suffolk	1 013 455	671 873	66
37	Barnet	999 580	732 799	73
38	Bedfordshire	977 864	658 526	67
39	Cumbria	977 849	626 812	64
40	Gloucestershire	966 204	483 134	50

DEVELOPING MENTAL MATHS

PHOTOCOPIABLE

JAM JAR SAVINGS

£7.30 £5.90 £5.70 £1.60

£1.10 £3.00 90P £3.40

20P £4.30 £4.80 £6.40

£2.50 £8.20 £9.00 £4.10

RAPID RECALL

Name

1	2	3	4	5	6	7	8	9	10
2									
3									
4									
5									
6									
7									
8									
9									
10									

Name

1	2	3	4	5	6	7	8	9	10
2									
3									
4									
5									
6									
7									
8									
9									
10									

RACETRACK GAMEBOARD

Start

$6 \div 3$ $36 \div 6$

$18 \div 2$ $20 \div 4$

2

$18 \div 6$ $21 \div 3$

3 $63 \div 9$

$56 \div 7$ $100 \div 10$

$81 \div 9$ $5 \div 1$

$24 \div 8$ **4**

$45 \div 5$ **5** $18 \div 3$

$42 \div 6$ $16 \div 4$

$42 \div 7$ **9**

$25 \div 5$ **6** $56 \div 8$

$27 \div 9$ $54 \div 6$

$49 \div 7$

$64 \div 8$ $56 \div 7$

7 **8**

$54 \div 9$ $14 \div 2$

$21 \div 7$ $60 \div 10$ $63 \div 7$ $24 \div 3$ $9 \div 3$

DEVELOPING MENTAL MATHS

SPIRAL GAMEBOARD

Fill in the spaces with numbers between 9 and 100.

DEVELOPING MENTAL MATHS

STOCK LIST

Accessories

Hat	£15.00
Scarf	£20.00
Gloves	£7.00
Socks	£3.00
Belt	£14.00
Tie	£8.00
Cufflinks	£14.00
Braces	£7.00
Shoelaces	£2.00
Tie pin	£12.00

Fashion

Shirt	£30.00
Coat	£70.00
Dress	£40.00
Trousers	£25.00
Jumper	£32.00
Dress suit	£186.00
Skirt	£33.00
Shorts	£19.00
Anorak	£27.00
Cardigan	£35.00

Perfumery

Perfume	£35.00
Aftershave	£22.00
Manicure set	£28.00
Shaving kit	£10.00
Face cream	£15.00
Electric razor	£20.00
Shaving mirror	£14.00
Lipstick	£8.00
Bath salts	£5.40
Mascara	£7.20

Food Hall

Champagne	£16.00
Caviar	£35.00
Fish fingers	£2.20
Leg of lamb	£8.80
Vintage port	£45.00
Olive oil	£7.40
String of garlic	£2.90
Biscuits	£1.40
Ice cream	£4.00
Lobster	£11.00

Furniture

Sofa	£300.00
Arm chair	£200.00
Dining table	£1500.00
Coffee table	£150.00
Bookshelf unit	£120.00
Bunk beds	£350.00
Double bed	£450.00
Wardrobe	£400.00
Mirror	£220.00
Sideboard	£380.00

Electrical Goods

Kettle	£20.00
Washer/drier	£350.00
Dishwasher	£450.00
Tumble drier	£380.00
Food mixer	£135.00
Coffee maker	£75.00
Teasmaid	£65.00
Iron	£48.00
Television	£170.00
Radio	£28.50

Gardening

Window box	£18.50
Fork	£20.25
Spade	£21.00
Wheelbarrow	£47.00
Patio set	£94.00
Barbecue	£68.00
Shed	£130.00
Gnome	£20.50
Pond liner	£18.20
Hose	£16.00

Travel Goods

Large suitcase	£64.00
Small suitcase	£46.00
Rucksack	£38.00
Daysack	£29.00
Suit bag	£53.00
Vanity case	£62.00
Suitcase set	£154.00
Money belt	£8.70
Briefcase	£84.00
Handbag	£30.00

Sports Equipment

Tennis racquet	£42.00
Squash racquet	£56.00
Exercise bike	£124.00
Ski machine	£126.00
Rollerblades	£88.00
Running shoes	£98.00
Wet suit	£54.00
Cricket bat	£71.00
Football	£25.00
Dumbbells	£28.00

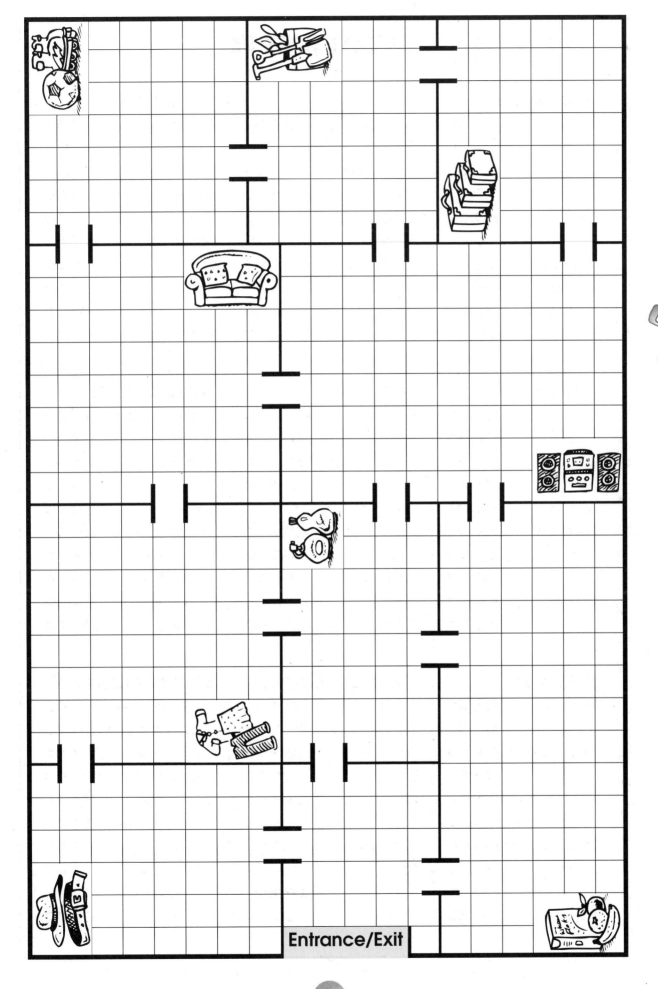

Entrance/Exit

MENTAL MATHS WRITING FRAME

Name

I have been working on...

Before I started the work I thought...

I have found out...

I also learned that...

One thing I will remember (or try to remember!) is...

Although I have learned...

I am still unsure about...

I would like to go on to do some work on...

Finally, I am pleased with myself because...